TREASURE

AT

TWENTY

FATHOMS

ALSO BY PATRICK O'CONNOR

The Society of Foxes
Flight of the Peacock
The Watermelon Mystery
Gunpowder for Washington
The Lost Harpooner
The Five-Dollar Watch Mystery
The Black Tiger
Mexican Road Race
Black Tiger at Le Mans
Black Tiger at Bonneville

TREASURE AT TWENTY FATHOMS

By Patrick O'Connor

Ives Washburn, Inc.   New York

DEDICATION

I want to thank Lieutenants Jack Wise, Don St. Hill, and Mickey O'Brien, of the Los Angeles County Lifeguards, who introduced me to the world of scuba diving and patiently steered me safely into it. It was they who gave me lessons in a swimming pool to start with, then took me down in calm water in the Pacific and finally down in the open ocean. They laid before me a treasure of the greatest beauty—the serene, silent, alluring underwater world. I would hate to have missed it. I will always be grateful to them for taking me into it.

To these men, then, and to my two friends Bob and Bill Miestrell, I offer this small book in gratitude for the great gift they gave me.

THE AUTHOR

Hermosa Beach,
California

I.

CHUCK CRAWFORD was walking along the stony part of the seashore at Redondo Beach, California, looking for whatever he might find. He was sixteen years of age, and this was a favorite occupation of his. Most of the beach to the north and south—named Redondo by the Spanish discoverers because of the magnificent round sweep of the bay—was of sand. But there was one area of stones, stones worn to the shape of eggs or marbles by the ceaseless coming and going of the sea. In this area it was possible to find many exciting things—opals, for instance, rounded moonlike opals, some of them as big as a thumbnail. They were not valuable. Gem opals were rare and none had ever been found at Redondo Beach to Chuck's knowledge. Still there was always the possibility of stumbling on one, and once polished the ordinary opals made an interesting collection.

[1]

Then there were jaspar and mock jade and other colored stones. Chuck often filled his pockets with such stones, took them home, and occasionally polished one or two, using the high-school equipment.

"Whatever do you bring all those stones home for?" his mother asked from time to time, sometimes with a touch of irritation because he kept them in his bedroom and they often fell on the floor and got under the bed and she had to sweep them out.

"Kid stuff," his father would say. "When I was your age . . ." And then would follow some statement of what his father had done when he was sixteen—raised pigeons and made money selling the squabs. Or he'd made five dollars a week collecting scrap lumber, and selling it as kindling. And he'd walked three miles to school and three miles back. There were no school buses in those days apparently, and Mr. Crawford seemed to take the view that a terrible blow had been struck both American education and the national character with the introduction of the school bus, and the placing of schools at distances of less than three miles from the nearest home.

"The trouble with dad and mom," Chuck said to himself, "is that they don't remember what it was like being sixteen years of age. But I know. It's like being lost or something. You just want to be alone and think and nobody gives you a chance. In school there're people stuffing you full of stuff. And at home if you sit down you're lazy and should be mowing the lawn. Or out playing ball. There just isn't any time to plain think."

When he had told himself this, Chuck felt better. Out among the stones on the beach, with the soft and soothing noise of the water flushing backward and forward among the pebbles, he had time to think. Not that he was very

[2]

much good at it. But at least he didn't have other people's thoughts and other people's desires constantly thrust on him. He was looking for something among the pebbles. He could kid himself that it was a gem opal but he was really trying to find himself in the morass of being sixteen years old.

Sometimes he believed that he would do great things in life, that the world had been, as it were, waiting for Chuck Crawford to be born and that later on he would be a very famous man. In this mood he was cheerful and confident, worked hard, and was willing both at school and around the house. But there was an opposite mood when he believed that no matter to what he put his hand and mind, he could not succeed; the odds were too great and his ability was too small. He'd be a nobody. And what was the sense of being born and learning all that stuff at school and going on to college to wind up a nobody?

His father was a nobody. He owned a paint store in Redondo Beach. What was the use of coming into the world and getting educated and working hard all your life to wind up owning a paint store in Redondo Beach?

Redondo Beach wasn't even a big town. So his father's wasn't a big paint store. Of course his father hadn't been to college. He seemed in fact almost proud of the fact that he'd only completed grade school and then gone to work.

"The Depression," his father said. "That's the college I learned in. When your mother and I were married all we had was a dollar and twenty-five cents and a T-Model Ford. And now I've got the best paint store in Redondo Beach and enough in the bank so that you don't have to worry."

"No sense in me going to college if you did so well without it," said Chuck.

[3]

"You'll go to college if it takes every cent I made to get you through," roared Mr. Crawford.

Thinking all this over, shuffling the stones on the beach with his foot, it didn't make much sense to Chuck. Not much that adults had to say did anyway. If you went through a depression it was better than going to college. And if all you had in the world was a dollar and twenty-five cents and an old car it was O.K. to get married. And his father was working hard to get a thousand-dollar paint contract from a new motel in town, when at any moment the world was likely to be blown to bits if the wrong person pressed a button somewhere. His father said so himself.

"I don't think people know any more when they're forty-five than they do when they're sixteen," said Chuck. "They're all mixed up."

He sat down on the beach to think about this, lowering his gangling five-foot-eleven inches onto the stones awkwardly. He considered his feet which, stretched out before him, commanded the view. They were too big. A year ago they seemed to fit all right, but now they were much too big for him. Even walking along he kept tripping on them. From contemplating his feet, he turned to his hands. They had grown big, too. He'd never looked at them closely before, but they were plainly about a half-size too big for his wrists.

"Jeepers," he said. "Where did I get those skinny wrists from?" He rolled up a short sleeve and examined his arm. It was a little better than his wrist. When he clenched his fist he could make the muscles come out. But they weren't what he'd call good muscles. They weren't anywhere near the right size for the length of his arm.

While he was engaged in this examination, Tom Prior walked past him down the beach and stood for a little

[4]

while at the water's edge looking around carefully and occasionally glancing up at the sky, shielding his eyes against the sun. Tom was a lifeguard, a blocky, well-built man with a chest that would have done credit to a bear. He was wearing the bright-red bathing trunks issued to the county lifeguards and everything about him, to Chuck's disgust, seemed to fit. His feet weren't too big and his hands weren't too big, and even standing still and doing no work, you could see the muscles on his arms and legs were good-sized.

When Tom had finished whatever inspection he had come down the beach to make, he turned and squatted beside Chuck. They knew each other well. In fact, Tom had trained Chuck in the junior lifeguard program when Chuck was a kid of ten.

"Something the matter with your arms?" Tom said, still looking out to sea. That was the way he always talked. He asked a question but always looked away somewhere, as if it wasn't really a question but just a chance remark.

"Nope," said Chuck. "I was just looking at them."

"Figured they were about to fall off or something?"

Chuck flushed. "They're the wrong size," he said. "They're kind of skinny for my hands. I guess I don't get enough exercise. My feet are too big, too," he added. And then he said quickly and passionately, "Everything's all mixed up."

"Meaning what?" asked Tom, still looking at the sea.

"Meaning that I don't know what anything's about. Nothing makes sense. Life and things like that. Being born. And all that."

For the first time Tom turned and looked at him. It was a slow calm look and kindly. "It's tough sometimes," he said.

[5]

The two of them remained in silence looking at the ocean for some time. Chuck didn't want to say anything further. He felt that Tom understood what his troubles were and that in any case they could not be explained further. It was sufficient, then, just to sit for a while.

The sun was almost ready to set and the water before them was a deep, purplish blue. The surf, breaking on the shore, was no longer the bone white of midday but tinged with a soft gold. The shoreward side of the waves, just before they broke, showed clear green like a glass bottle. The water was so clear that they could see in each wave, as it lifted up to break, the dark delicate lines of bits of seaweed, imprisoned for a second in the transparent green. There was something lovely in the sight.

"I was figuring on going scuba diving tonight," said Tom, after a while. "Might get a white sea bass or a halibut. Like to come along for the ride?"

"Sure," said Chuck, very fast, before he thought of what his parents' reaction would be. "But I'd want to go diving, too."

"We'll be using Pee Wee's boat," said Tom. "We'll try in the harbor for a while for halibut and then go round the breakwater and see what else we can find."

"I haven't got a lung," said Chuck.

Tom picked up a pebble and threw it a few feet ahead of him. "Who taught you to use scuba?" he asked.

"Nobody," said Chuck. "But it's easy. I'm a good swimmer and I've done a lot of skin diving—snorkel, faceplate, and fins. Scuba's easier because you don't have to come up for air. You've got the air on your back in a tank. It's a cinch."

"You ever used scuba?"

[6]

"No. But I don't see that there's any magic to it. Just put the mouthpiece in your mouth and go down. Easy."

Tom didn't comment on this immediately. Instead he got slowly to his feet and said, "Want to come over to the lifeguard station with me? I got some equipment over there you could look at."

Chuck grunted and the two went over to the lifeguard station, which was perhaps a quarter of a mile down the beach. When they arrived, Tom opened a door at the back of the garage where the lifeguard trucks were housed. It revealed a room whose walls were completely taken up by shelves. On the shelves were various items of scuba diving equipment—rubber wetsuits, faceplates, weight belts, regulators, and racks of air tanks. Standing against the shelves at one end were a number of other tanks. They were obviously old, the gray galvanized surface marked by barnacle shells; some had a few wisps of dried marine growth still clinging to them.

"How would you like to use one of those tanks?" asked Tom softly.

"You kidding?" said Chuck. "They look like they've been lying in the bottom of the ocean for months."

"They were," said Tom. "We found them on the bodies, or rather what was left of the bodies, of drowned scuba divers." He brought forward a tank on which the barnacle growth was particularly heavy.

"This one here," he said, "had been down two and a half years when we found it. Probably a record for these parts. We were able to identify the diver by the number stamped on the tank. Name was Greenwright, Henry Greenwright. Age thirty-four, married, had a wife and four kids. Lived in Pacoima. He came down here to Re-

[7]

dondo Beach after looking at a lot of those TV movies about skin diving, and decided there was nothing to it and he could dive himself. He was a good swimmer. He rented his equipment. Cost him eight bucks. Then he went over to Catalina Island, put on his rubber suit and his gear, waded into the water—and drowned.''

"Nitrogen narcosis?" asked Chuck, who had done some reading on the subject of scuba diving.

"Forget about nitrogen narcosis," said Tom. "Just plain ignorance. And panic. Probably got a little water in his tube and didn't know how to clear it. The tank itself is in perfect shape and so was his regulator.''

"Two and a half years later?" demanded Chuck.

"Yeah," said Tom, "two and a half years later. I put that tank on myself and took it down in my swimming pool and it worked like a charm. You want to take it diving tonight?"

"Not likely," said Chuck.

"Superstitious?" asked Tom. "Or are you not quite so sure that you know how to use scuba?"

"Well . . ." said Chuck, "from what I'd heard and seen, it seemed easy.''

"Well, it isn't easy," said Tom. "It's hard because as soon as you get your head down in the water you're in another world where you really ought not to be. And any silly little move you make that is wrong could kill you. Like sneezing. You can sneeze on land and live to a ripe old age. But if you sneeze underwater you may—I don't say you will—but you may blow your mouthpiece out of your mouth, get water in the tubes if you are using the old-style equipment, fail to clear the water, and drown.

"And it isn't only amateurs who kill themselves. Experienced scuba divers get drowned, too—when they're

[8]

behaving like amateurs and taking chances they have been trained not to take. Have a look at this tank here.''

He dragged out another tank, quite clean of marine growth compared with the first. "See here?" said Tom, pointing with his finger to a valve at the top. "That's the reserve air-supply valve. Pulled down by this wire, it supplies about five minutes more air to the diver if his main tank is empty.

"Now notice that this diver had opened his emergency supply valve. See the marking of that barnacle shell? Part of it is on the stationary part of the tank and part of it is on the movable valve. The marking fits when the valve is down in the used position. So this guy was on the bottom, knew he was running out of air, and pulled his reserve air-supply valve down as he should. And he still drowned.''

"Why?" asked Chuck.

"Diving alone," said Tom. "I knew this diver well. As a matter of fact he gave me my first lessons in scuba diving about ten years ago. 'Don't ever dive alone,' he used to say.

"But he didn't take his own advice. He'd dived alone for years and figured he was the exception to his own rule. Well, he got into some trouble on the bottom, used up his air, turned on his reserve, used that up. Then he drowned. If he'd had a buddy with him, he'd be alive today.

"What do you say? Want to borrow some of this equipment and go scuba diving tonight?"

"Uh, uh," said Chuck.

"Now you're getting smart," said Tom. "Tell you what I'll do. I'll give you lessons—the whole course. But you'll have to go all the way through with it and learn everything I tell you, even if you think it's kind of stupid.''

"Swell," said Chuck. "When can we start?"

[9]

"Couple of days," said Tom. "Be down here tonight at nine and you can handle the boat for Pee Wee and me while we do a little spear hunting."

They went out of the lifeguard station together and just as they were about to part Tom, looking out at the ocean as if he weren't talking to Chuck at all, said "Things still seem kind of tough?"

Chuck didn't reply. He stood looking at the ocean rolling smoothly and powerfully toward the shore. He was wondering what it was like down there at the bottom in the silent, green, impersonal depths.

He felt afraid. But he knew that he must go down into the depths of the sea—that there was something there of value to him.

II.

THREE DAYS LATER Chuck met Tom Prior at his house. It was a Friday night and Tom had told Chuck not to eat much dinner.

"I'm going to start giving you those lessons I promised in scuba diving," he said. "You'll have a pretty tough workout in the pool. Best not to have a full stomach."

"What do you want me to bring?" Chuck asked.

"Just some swim trunks and a towel," said Tom.

Chuck felt disappointed. He'd hoped he would be told to rent some scuba gear. Just swim trunks didn't sound very exciting.

He was standing now on the side of the pool with Tom, who was sorting through a pile of fins, snorkels, and faceplates. He picked up a faceplate, spat in the interior, dipped it in the pool and rinsed it off.

Chuck began to feel a little superior. He knew all about

that procedure. It was done to prevent the glass of the faceplate misting up under water. He knew about diving with snorkel and faceplate. He'd done it many times. He had hoped that he would be given a tank and a regulator and instructed in their use.

Tom, if he saw the look of superiority on Chuck's face, did not react to it. He threw the faceplate into the deep end of the pool—ten feet of water—and said. "Go down and get that. Put it on underwater and come up with it in position on your head."

"What? All full of water?" asked Chuck.

"Do the best you can," said Tom. Chuck dived cleanly into the water, located the faceplate, which was just a blurred blue object on the bottom, tried to put it on his head, but his own buoyancy brought him to the surface before he had succeeded. He finally got it on, and it was half-full of water so that, though there was air in the portion over his eyes, there was water in the portion covering his nostrils.

"Take it off," said Tom, and Chuck did so.

"You ever learned how to clear your faceplate under water?" Tom asked, squatting on the side of the pool. "I mean blow out the water from it while submerged?"

"No," said Chuck. "If my faceplate fills up when I'm snorkeling, I just surface and empty it."

"Well, that's O.K. for snorkeling," said Tom. "But what would you do if you were down say ten fathoms, and another diver kicked your faceplate off, and it filled full of water? The water inside your faceplate would make it impossible for you to see very far. What would you do about that?"

"Come up and clear it?" asked Chuck, not feeling quite so superior.

[12]

Tom shook his head. "No," he said. "You have to clear it under water. Now here's what you do. First of all, you've got that thing on upside down. There's a top and a bottom to a faceplate. On most of them the bolt holding the glass in place in the rubber body is on top. You got that?" asked Tom.

"Yes," said Chuck.

"Well, remember it. The first thing you do with a faceplate is locate that bolt and see that you get the thing on right side up. Otherwise it will leak. Now, about clearing it. You put your hand on the right side of the faceplate, press gently, roll on your left side and look up toward the surface, and then blow through your nostrils. The air will blow the water out at the bottom of the faceplate—that is, at the left side. Let's see if I can put that more clearly. Your hand is on the right side—by your right eye. Got it?"

"Yes."

"Good. You roll over on your left, look upward, and blow through your nostrils. The water then goes out of the left side of the faceplate—the side near your left eye."

"Why?" asked Chuck.

"Good question," said Tom. "By putting pressure on the right side, you slightly diminish the pressure on the left side. By blowing air into the faceplate you force the water to move. The only place it can move out is through that area of diminished pressure—the left side. Now. Let's see you dive down there again, put that faceplate on, right side up, mind you, and blow the water out. Then come to the surface."

"What am I supposed to do for air after I've blown all the air in my lungs into the faceplate?" asked Chuck.

"Your lungs hold many times the amount of air you

[13]

can get into that faceplate," said Tom. "Don't worry. You'll have plenty left—if you don't waste it."

Tom took the faceplate and threw it into the pool. It sank slowly and when it was on the bottom, Chuck dived in after it. He found it readily enough, put it on, found himself floating to the top, struggled to the bottom again, turned on his side, put his right hand on the right side of the faceplate, and blew into it through his nostrils.

Immediately a flock of bubbles flooded out of the faceplate from all around the edges. He had to struggle to keep on the bottom. He kept on blowing until he was out of breath and then surfaced. The faceplate was still half-full of water and Tom was grinning at him from the side of the pool.

"Doesn't work," spluttered Chuck. "I blew into it until I could see little lights exploding all over the place and there's still water."

"You've got it on upside down," said Tom.

"Aw, nuts," said Chuck, feeling for the little bolt which should be at the top of the glass if the faceplate was on right. It was on the bottom.

"The big thing about doing anything under water," said Tom seriously, "is to figure out beforehand what you have to do. I mean figure it out in detail. You have to dive in. You have to find the faceplate. You have to locate that bolt. Then you have to put the faceplate on right way up. Only then do you start clearing it. Ready to try again?"

"Yes," said Chuck.

This time he did better. He got the faceplate on right way up, but didn't get all the water out of it.

"I did exactly what you told me, but it doesn't work," he said.

"Empty the water, put the faceplate on, and come down

and watch me," said Tom. Chuck did so. With his face-plate clear of water, he could see all around the pool quite clearly. He saw Tom dive to the bottom, casually pick a faceplate from it, feel for the top, put it on, and then roll on his side. Tom put his hand quite slowly to the side of the faceplate and as if by a miracle it started to drain of water. Only a few bubbles of air escaped. They surfaced together.

"Not much air got out," said Chuck.

"Right," said Tom. "The object is to drive the water out. You don't need more than a cupful of air to do it. You're having trouble because you are pressing with your hand too hard. That makes a big opening on the opposite side and the air gets out with the water. You shouldn't make an opening at all—just an area where the pressure of the plate against your face is less than at other parts. The water will be forced out of that area. Try again and I'll watch you."

This time Chuck succeeded in clearing the faceplate entirely of water. He wasn't even out of breath and felt that he could easily have stayed down a minute more.

"Good," said Tom. "Now go ahead and practice that for a while. I'm going into the house for a minute to have a cup of coffee."

Chuck would have liked a cup of coffee himself, but said nothing. He concentrated on diving for the faceplate, putting it on under water, and clearing it. He discovered that the more relaxed he was about the whole process the easier it was to do. When Tom came back after his coffee, Chuck was feeling like an expert.

"Learn anything?" asked Tom.

"Sure. I learned how to get the water out of the thing."

"Anything else?"

[15]

"Well, how to put it on right under water."

"Anything else?"

"Wasn't anything else to learn," said Chuck.

"There were a couple more things," said Tom. "Very important things. Did you notice that when you were not overanxious—excited—your breath lasted longer?"

"Yes," said Chuck.

"When you get excited—nervous, anxious, frightened or worried—you burn up more oxygen," said Tom. "That doesn't matter on land where there's plenty of oxygen available, but it matters a lot under water. Staying calm is the easiest way to stay down a long time and the easiest way to get out of trouble. That's one thing. The second thing I've told you before. Whenever you have to do anything under water, think it out on land first. In detail. It's easy to think on land. There's plenty of time. In the water it's about four times as hard."

"Why?" asked Chuck.

Tom shrugged. "I'm no doctor," he said, "and even doctors guess about it. But for one thing, you're in a completely foreign element. Everything's strange. That may distract your power of concentration, which is one of the most important parts of thinking.

"Then there's pressure. My theory is that it cuts down the blood circulation to the brain. Maybe I'm all wet on this but that's my theory. Anyway, at fifteen feet under the water you don't think anywhere near as fast as you do on the surface.

"I had a guy once who didn't believe that. He was sure that he thought just as well under water as he did on the surface. His name was Sam. So I gave him a board and grease pencil and had him put on his gear and go down fifteen feet in a swimming pool and write his name on the

[16]

board—backward. He was down twenty minutes and finally he came up. He couldn't do it."

"Must have been some kind of idiot," said Chuck.

"No," said Tom, "just pressure. When men are working under water, they rehearse everything they have to do on land first, if they're smart. You take salvage divers. If they have to undo a bolt on a hatch, for instance, at a hundred and sixty feet, they practice doing it on land over and over again, so that it's an automatic reflex when they're actually down there. They can do it without thinking. But they get all fuddled up if the bolt's in the wrong place or they drop the wrench."

"You ever worked that deep?" asked Chuck.

"Yes," said Tom.

"On a wreck?"

"Nope. Looking for a lady's handbag. There was a watch with a diamond bracelet worth about two thousand dollars in it."

"Did you find it?"

"I found the handbag. I was lucky to find that. There was a hole ripped in the side of it and no watch. I guess some lobster got curious and went off with it. Someday some scuba diver is going to find a lobster wearing a two-thousand-dollar watch walking around on the bottom of the ocean, and if he's got any sense he'll keep his mouth shut because nobody is ever going to believe him. You ready for some more of the lesson?"

"Yes," said Chuck. "Let's go."

Tom picked up a thick block of plastic which was lying by the pool. It was the size of a large brick and there were two plates of lead through the middle of it. He threw it into the deep end.

"That's a ten-pound lobster," he said. "Go down and

[17]

get it. Pick it up and swim up to the surface without kicking off from the bottom. Remember you are not to put your feet on the bottom and push off for the surface. You are to swim up.''

Chuck was a very good swimmer, but he found that, deprived of the use of his hands, which were holding the ten-pound ''lobster,'' and forbidden to kick off from the bottom, he had a hard struggle to swim to the surface. He was almost out of breath by the time he got there.

''You're struggling too hard,'' said Tom. ''The more you struggle, the more oxygen you use up and the shorter time you can stay down. The basic rule for underwater work is *take it easy*. Throw that thing in again and watch me.''

Chuck threw the block of plastic back into the pool, and Tom dived for it. Chuck put his head under water, and having his faceplate on, was able to see as readily as if he were looking into a fish tank. He saw Tom slide gracefully down toward the chunk of plastic, circle it, reach out slowly and get it. Then he rolled over on his back, put the block of plastic against his chest, and with two lazy movements of his flippers, glided up to the top.

''Get the idea?'' asked Tom.

''Yep,'' said Chuck. He tried again several times until he could retrieve the plastic block with ease.

''I know you've done a lot of snorkel diving,'' said Tom. ''But there is a big difference in scuba diving. Snorkel diving is a sport of its own and I do a lot of it myself. But the big thing about it is that when you've run out of breath, you come up, clear your snorkel, and start breathing. If you run out of breath scuba diving, it may be a real long way up to the top—sixty or seventy feet maybe. Or even more. And you've got to know what to do.''

"Why would you run out of breath if you've got a tank with air on your back?" asked Chuck.

"You might get caught down there and only get free when you've used up your air. Then you have to come to the top with what you have in your lungs. Or you might be relying on your reserve air supply and discover that either the valve didn't work or you had the valve in the open position when you went down, and so there isn't any reserve air supply. The main point is: What do you do if you run out of air in say sixty or seventy feet of water? That means sixty or seventy feet to go before you can get to the top and start breathing again."

He produced an aqualung tank—a steel cylinder, with straps around it for holding it in place on the diver's back, and a valve on the top.

"This is full of compressed air," he said. "Air at a pressure of two thousand five hundred pounds per square inch.

"If I were to drop this and knock that valve off the top, this container would go clean through the wall of my house as well as the wall of the house next door. So when you're handling one of these think of it as a bomb. Handle it gently. If you have to load one in the back of your car, be sure that the valve is protected from bumps and that the valve end of it is facing the rear of the car. If the valve breaks, the valve unit will rocket out of the back of the car, and not forward, probably killing you and whoever else may be sitting up front. Don't fool with these things. As I said before, they're like bombs. Handle them with respect."

"Why so much pressure?" asked Chuck.

"To cancel out the pressure on the diver when he is under water," said Tom. "The deeper a diver goes, the

[19]

more pressure there is on him. At six feet under water the pressure is so much that a man with a tube in his mouth to the surface cannot suck air through it. His muscles cannot expand his chest against the pressure of the water around sufficiently to suck in air from the surface. That's why hard-hat divers have to have air pumped down to them. And scuba divers carry compressed air—two thousand five hundred pounds per square inch—so that whatever depth they go to, they can get air regularly.

"Of course the air has to be metered by a regulator. The regulator adjusts itself automatically to the surrounding water pressure. If you're down say thirty-three feet, the pressure on your chest is around twenty-nine pounds per square inch. The regulator delivers air to you at that pressure so that there is no more effort to breathing than if you were on the surface.

"But here's the danger. On the surface the air in your lungs is at fourteen point seven pounds per square inch. Thirty-three feet down, with a mechanical lung, the air in your lungs is over twenty-nine pounds per square inch. Come quickly to the surface with that kind of pressure in your lungs and guess what happens?"

"Lungs explode?" asked Chuck.

"Right. You rip the walls of the lungs and you can be permanently injured. Or you can die. We were talking about running out of air on the bottom. Suppose you are down a hundred feet. What air you have in your lungs at that depth is at a pressure of around sixty-nine pounds per square inch. If you panic because you've run out of air and rocket to the top, your lungs will explode. You'll die anyway—and very painfully. What you have to do to save your lungs and your life is come up fast but breathe out hard all the way."

"Breathe out all the way—when you're out of breath anyway?" demanded Chuck.

"You're not following me," said Tom. "You've got a lung full of air at nearly seventy pounds of pressure. Maybe it doesn't feel like that. Maybe you feel you're going to choke for lack of air. But actually your lungs are full though the oxygen content may be low.

"What you have to do is to fight back the panicky feeling that you're going to suffocate and start up with your head tilted back, your mouth wide open, and breathing out all the way. You have to get that air in your lungs down to fourteen pounds per square inch pressure when you hit the surface or you split your lungs."

"You ever had to do that?" asked Chuck.

"No," said Tom. "But that doesn't mean I never will have to—or you either."

III.

TWO NIGHTS a week, Mondays and Thursdays, Tom had standby duty at lifeguard headquarters at Redondo Beach. He shared this duty with two other lifeguards, Buzzie Harper and Pee Wee Millstein. Of the trio, Buzzie was the most adventurous. He loved all water sports, had competed in the Olympics in the breast stroke division, gaining second place, went yearly to Hawaii for surfing and had even gone to New Zealand where he had introduced the art of riding a surfboard in one part of New Zealand and had become a local hero—or so he claimed.

"They'd do anything for me in New Zealand," he told Tom. "I ran out of money and I knew you guys wouldn't send me any . . ."

"Wonder how he knew that," said Tom innocently to Pee Wee.

". . . I knew you guys wouldn't send me any," continued Buzzie, "because you're always borrowing yourselves. Talking about borrowing, where's that five bucks you were supposed to pay me back last week?"

"I sent it to New Zealand," said Tom. "Figured you might want it when you get back there and they make you mayor of that one-horse town you were in. But go on with your story. I haven't heard any fairy stories since I sat at my mother's knee."

"Well, I ran out of money," said Buzzie, "and I started a business making surfboards and sold enough to pay my fare back here to the States. The business is still going and when I get back to that part of the world I'll be set for life. No more of this spending my time warning little kids away from riptides, telling visitors that there are no man-eating sharks off the beach in these parts, and devoting two nights a week down here trying to teach you dumb clucks how to play chess."

"We'll sure miss you," said Pee Wee. "No laughs at all. Nobody to take a fifteen-week driving course and then back the ambulance into a lamp post. . . ."

"Nobody to launch the dory like a hero and put to sea with only one oar in it," said Tom.

"Nobody to give a lecture on accident prevention and break a collarbone getting down off the podium," said Pee Wee.

"Why don't you two guys go jump in the ocean?" demanded Buzzie.

"Because," said Pee Wee seriously, "that would leave no one here to look after you. You know what the captain said: 'Keep an eye on Buzzie. He's the biggest hazard in the whole city.' "

"When I get back to New Zealand—" said Buzzie.

[23]

"We'll cable ahead and tell them to have an ambulance ready," said Tom.

"Pipe down," said Pee Wee, "there's something coming over the loud-speaker."

It took a trained ear to tell what it was. By no means a talented instrument, it reduced the human voice to something akin to the squawkings of a parrot. The broadcasts came on short wave from the police, and the lifeguards listened because among their duties was that of applying artificial respiration to people who had suffered heart attacks and assisting the police and hospital services of the city generally.

"Private plane with two men aboard believed down off Palos Verdes," said the flattened voice on the loud-speaker. "Coast Guard helicopter is checking the area—"

At this point the telephone rang and Tom picked it up.

"Tom," said the voice on the other end which he recognized as Captain Williams, his chief, "you want to make a dive tonight?"

"You mean that airplane?" asked Tom.

"Yep."

"They don't expect those guys to be alive, do they?" asked Tom.

"No," said Captain Williams, "but the passenger was a top executive for the Cobalt Bearing Company."

"So?" said Tom.

"They make rocket parts," said Williams. "He had an attaché case along with some specifications in it. They want the attaché case quick, before there's too much spoilage from the water."

"What about the bodies?" asked Tom. "They want them brought up now? You know what it's like down there with just a flashlight to work with."

[24]

"No. They will have to wait. It's the attaché case that's important now. Well, what do you say? You know the rules. You don't have to dive if you don't feel like it, and as you know, nobody will think any the worse of you."

"Give me a minute," said Tom. He turned to Buzzie, who was sitting across the table from him. He said nothing but just looked at Buzzie, and Buzzie nodded his head.

"O.K.," said Tom, "Buzzie will go with me."

"Good," said Captain Williams. "I'll send a relief over for you. Meanwhile there's nothing for you to do but check your gear and wait until the Coast Guard get a fix on the plane. I'll radio them and they'll come over and get you in their cutter."

Tom hung up, walked from the room in which they were sitting to a small kitchen to the side, poured himself a cup of coffee, and came back with it. Buzzie and Pee Wee knew enough not to speak to him for a few minutes. When Tom was ready, he would start talking.

Tom took a meditative sip of his coffee, went over to a chart of the area pinned on the wall, squinted at it, traced a line offshore from Palos Verdes with his stubby finger, and said, "About a hundred and eighty feet, I'd say. We'll take twin tanks with a small extra tank fitted with its own regulator just in case."

"Is it going to be a quick dive or will we be down there some time and have to decompress?" asked Buzzie.

"Quick dive, I hope," said Tom. "I'm not going down until the Coast Guard has a pretty good fix on the plane. No more looking for airplane wreckage among those rocks in pitch dark and likely to bump into something and knock your brains out."

"The brains part wouldn't trouble Buzzie," said Pee Wee.

[25]

"Why don't you go jump in the ocean?" asked Buzzie for the second time that night.

"That's just what you're going to do," said Pee Wee. "I got more sense."

"O.K.," said Tom, ignoring the banter. "Twin tanks with a small reserve tank. Lights and about six feet of rope. And a jimmy apiece because that cockpit will be jammed shut. They always are."

"And a shark billie," said Buzzie. "I got one made of a baseball bat with nails studding the end of it. Made it up after the last time. Remember?"

Tom nodded. Remember? He would never forget. They had gone down after another pilot and the sharks were as thick as flies in a stable. There had been one blue shark that circled them twice and then came in, straight as an arrow, for his attack.

Tom had put his under-water knife out in front of him, held at arm's length, and the shark had driven straight at it, pushing him fifteen feet through the water, his charge was so fast. Then he'd gone off with Tom's knife sticking in his snout. And that had been in the daylight when they could see around them. This would be at night, and sharks were far more active at night.

"Let's check our gear," he said to Buzzie. They went to the big locker room where the diving equipment was kept.

"Wonder what's so all-fired important about those papers that they want them up right away," said Buzzie, taking a two-unit tank down from its rack. He put a pressure gauge on it, opened the valve, and noted the pressure was a shade under twenty-five hundred pounds per square inch.

"Your guess is as good as mine," said Tom. "We'll never know anyway. If they're that secret, all we do is

[26]

hand over the attaché case and that's all we'll ever hear of it. How much weight you using?"

"Fifteen pounds," replied Buzzie. "That's about what I need for that depth."

"We shouldn't have to decompress," said Tom. "That's something to be thankful for. I don't fancy hanging on a line in that freezing water, not able to see a thing, waiting to be decompressed."

"Trouble with you is you're scared of the dark," said Buzzie.

"It's the things that bump into you in the dark that scare me," said Tom. "When we're down there, don't you come up behind and tap me or you'll probably get a knife through your arm. All signals with lights."

"Don't worry about a thing," said Buzzie. "Remember that there are two of us. If there are any sharks around, there's a fifty per cent chance they'll take you instead of me. That's what I like about the buddy system of diving."

Both men were checking their equipment while chatting away. Although all the equipment owned by the lifeguards was periodically checked by experts, it was a habit for Tom and Buzzie to make their own inspection before each dive. They looked the harness of their lungs over carefully for wear, examined the rubber hoses through which they would breathe and exhale, foot by foot, for defects, especially at the point where they were hooked to the regulator. Then they connected them to the tanks, listened carefully for air leaks at the junction, and took a couple of breaths through the mouthpieces to see that all was working well. They found no faults and took down their rubber suits from the clothes hangers on which they were kept and headed for the dressing room.

"Guess we might as well get into these," said Buzzie.

[27]

"You got any talcum powder?" asked Tom.

"I thought you had it," said Buzzie.

"Cripes," said Tom. "I thought we agreed last time that you'd bring the talc."

"Other way around," said Buzzie. "You were going to bring it."

"Don't tell me I have to get into this wetsuit again without any talc," groaned Tom.

"Life is full of troubles like that," said Buzzie. "Just wet yourself under the shower, son, and it won't be so tough. Of course, there's no hot water. Something went wrong with the heater and it hasn't been fixed yet."

"Great," said Tom. He stripped down, turned on the shower, stepped into the freezing deluge with his rubber suit in his arms, and wetted that thoroughly. Then, shivering, he got out and started to put on the pants. With talcum powder as a lubricant, they could be got on readily enough. But without talcum powder or corn starch, they went on only with much struggling, though the water helped a little.

When Tom had got his pants on and was struggling into his rubber jacket, he turned to Buzzie. Buzzie, to his surprise, already had on his rubber pants.

"How did you get into them?" demanded Tom.

"You were right," said Buzzie.

"I was right about what?"

"About the talcum powder. You said I had agreed to bring it and you were right. I'd forgotten. Then I remembered that I'd brought it. But you were all wet and shivering already, old buddy, so I just used it myself."

"Get out of here!" roared Tom and flung a sopping towel at him.

"It was just a little mistake," said Buzzie, dodging. "Could happen to anybody."

When they returned to the duty room of the lifeguard station, Captain Williams had just arrived with the two men who would relieve them while they dived.

"The Coast Guard has got a good fix on the plane," he said. "There's an oil slick coming up from it and they've been able to locate it with grappling tackle, but they don't want to try to lift it in case it comes apart and the papers get lost. But you'll have a line to go down and won't have to search the bottom for the wreckage."

"Good," said Tom. "Now is there any dope on where those papers are likely to be? Would they be beside the passenger or in a special compartment or what?"

"I've checked on that with the company. The papers are in an attaché case, as you know. There's a chain from the handle of the case which is fastened around the wrist of the passenger. His name is Ridder, if that matters. The chain business is standard practice for the company. When anyone is carrying a dispatch case with important papers in it, they must have this chain from the handle around a wrist, in case someone tries to snatch the case."

"Be a pretty strong chain?" asked Tom.

"No. One of those snaky deals without links in it. I've got a key with which you can unlock it from Ridder's wrist." He produced a small key and gave it to Tom. "If it doesn't work, do the best you can," he said.

"O.K.," said Tom.

"Best get out on the jetty," said Captain Williams. "The Coast Guard cutter will be over any minute. Some of you guys help carry down these tanks and weight belts. You want me to call Mary?" This was to Tom. Mary was Tom's wife.

"Nope," said Tom, "no sense worrying her. With any luck I'll be back home at the regular time."

"Can I go with you?" It was Chuck Crawford speaking.

[29]

"How did you get here?" asked Captain Williams, who knew Chuck.

"I was listening in on my shortwave set and heard about it," said Chuck.

"Well, this is an official deal," said Williams. "You'd better not go along. You might be in the way."

"Let him come," said Tom. "I'm teaching him to dive. It won't do him any harm. He can make sure that those Coast Guard boys have some coffee handy when we come up again."

"Gee, thanks," said Chuck with such sincerity that Captain Williams looked at him curiously.

"Let's go," said Buzzie. "I've lost five pounds already standing around with this rubber suit on."

They picked up their gear, the relief men and Chuck helping, and walked out of the station in the direction of the jetty to board the Coast Guard cutter.

IV.

A LIGHTED BUOY had been placed over the site of the plane wreck by the Coast Guard cutter. It bobbed and rolled on the surface of the night-black sea and was readily sighted by the cutter, which came alongside the buoy and lowered a bow anchor. The officer in charge of the cutter reported a depth of twenty fathoms —a hundred and twenty feet—and added they had made a run over the area with their Fathometer and there was a maze of reefs on the bottom.

"We're pretty sure we're right over the plane," he told Tom. "You can see the oil and gasoline slick on the surface, and the grappling hooks are caught on something that moves, so it isn't a rock. If there's anything else we can do, let us know."

"Just keep the coffeepot boiling," said Tom with a grin. "It'll be about forty degrees down there at this time of the year. If you can switch on your searchlights and direct them down into the sea, that would be a big help. The water seems clear and the searchlights may give us some illumination on the bottom. We'll go off the stern of the cutter. All set, Buzzie?''

Buzzie nodded. He had been leaning over the side, washing his faceplate out so that it wouldn't fog up. The two struggled into their tank harness and then put on their cumbersome weight belts.

''Weight belt goes on last,'' said Tom to Chuck who was standing near him. ''That way, if you have to drop it to surface in a hurry, it's clear and doesn't get hooked up in anything.''

He shuffled with Buzzie to the stern of the cutter, enormously clumsy with the big fins on his feet. Both had put on cotton work-gloves which gave a ridiculous clownish effect to their otherwise sinister appearance. The gloves would protect their hands from sharp coral or metal. Under water, the human skin softens greatly and is readily cut on anything sharp.

Tom selected a spot near the stern, sat down with his back to the water, put the regulator mouthpiece in his mouth, and took a couple of breaths. In the silence the sharp whistling intake of the air was clearly heard. Then he put a gloved hand firmly over his faceplate and rolled over backward into the sea, hitting the water with a solid splash.

The steel tank on his back took the shock of the impact and his hand on the faceplate prevented it being loosened and filled with water.

Buzzie followed immediately. For a second or two they were gone and then they reappeared, only their heads showing, and swam cumbersomely to the buoy from which

[32]

a line led down to the wreck. Chuck saw Tom signal with his clenched fist, his thumb pointed downward to the bottom. Buzzie nodded. The two surface-dived, their rubber-clad legs with black flippers showing weirdly for a moment in the glare of the searchlights. Then they were gone and on the spot where they had dived there was only a constant eruption of bubbles.

Captain Williams glanced at his watch. "Ten-fifteen," he announced. "With luck the job should be done in twenty minutes."

Chuck was peering into the lighted area around the buoy, made brilliant by the searchlights of the cutter. He was trying to follow the two divers going down but could see nothing except their bubbles bursting on the surface. His heart was thumping and his mouth was dry with excitement. Suddenly, in the illuminated area, there was a heavy swirl in the water as a fish broke through the surface and fell back with a splash. It seemed to be a big fish, but was glimpsed for only a second.

"The light attracts them," said Captain Williams. "There'll be more in a minute." Soon the water seemed to be boiling, with fish cutting darting patterns through the illuminated area.

"Must be thick with them down below," said Chuck.

Williams grunted. "Fish don't bother them," he said. "Just sharks."

"Sharks?" echoed Chuck. He'd forgotten about sharks.

"Yes," said Captain Williams. "If there's any blood, they'll be around. They can scent it from miles away."

Chuck said nothing more, wondering what it was like in the silence down there looking for a wrecked plane with two dead men aboard, with sharks, perhaps, gathering in the dark cold waters around.

[33]

Tom always had difficulty equalizing the pressure in his left ear. His right ear equalized readily enough, but the membrane lining the Eustachian tube in his left ear was chronically inflamed. The inflammation was not serious. It was just a nuisance, giving him trouble each time he dived. And he was having this trouble now.

Fifteen feet below the surface, he felt a growing pain in the ear and stopped, holding on to the line from the buoy. First he tried swallowing to clear the pain and equalize the pressure but without much effect. Then he wiggled his jaw from side to side. That sometimes helped but not this time. He pushed his faceplate hard against his face and blew into it through his nostrils. There was a lessening of the pain but not enough. The pressure he could build up in the faceplate wasn't sufficient to open the Eustachian tube.

Only one thing for it then. He took his faceplate off, grabbed his nostrils, and blew into them hard. He was rewarded by a click in his ear as the pressure equalized. He replaced the faceplate, cleared it of water using the technique he had taught Chuck in the swimming pool, and continued his descent. Twice more on the way down he had to equalize the pressure in his eardrums, but once the passage through the Eustachian tube was open, he could clear by swallowing.

He was going down the line head first, hand over hand. Normally he went down lines feet first because the head first method brought the blood to his head, and made him feel dizzy. In this case, however, diving at night and using a lamp on his forehead, he had to be able to see where he was going. At twenty feet or thereabouts the temperature of the water changed abruptly. It became very much colder and he could feel the shock of it on his face and

[34]

hands. The rest of his body was protected by his rubber wetsuit. But moving his head to see if he could get a glimpse of Buzzie above him, a jet of cold water made its way down the neck of the wetsuit along his naked spine.

"Rapture of the deep," he said to himself. "If it's this cold here, it must be solid ice on the bottom. Maybe it's snowing down there."

He had a habit of talking to himself while diving, and kept up a running commentary in his mind on everything he saw.

"You know what this is like?" he asked himself. "It's like visiting eternity. You keep on going and you get nowhere. There're seven links of chain I can see ahead. And every time I pull myself down, there're still the same seven links of chain ahead. So I don't gain anything. Sure is a weird feeling. All I can see are the same seven links of chain. Nothing else. Just a kind of fuzzy light from my lamp that disappears into nothing. Seven links and seven links and seven links. Be kind of funny if this led down into a deep hole right into the middle of the earth and we kept on following it seven links at a time. If I had any brains I'd have counted those links. They're about two inch links, and seven times two inches is fourteen inches. So that's about a foot at a time every hand hold. One hundred and twenty hand holds and I should be at the plane. Makes you dizzy standing on your head like this. Think I'll try it the other way for a while, right side up. Get tired of watching that chain going into the nowhere."

He upended himself so that he could see Buzzie a few feet above him. He waited on the chain until Buzzie reached him and then they started going down, feet first, but closer together. Tom could feel the glass of his faceplate pressing against the end of his nose because of the

[35]

pressure of the water outside. That happened at about ten fathoms—sixty feet. Another sixty feet to go and they'd be there.

It was utterly dark now. Looking up he could see a faint luminescence above where the searchlights played on the water. Other than that, the only thing visible was the blob of Buzzie's light. He couldn't even see Buzzie except for his light. He couldn't see the chain, but had to feel for it hand over hand. It was just as if he had his eyes closed in a dark room. That was about as much as he could see. A cold dark room with all kinds of unknown creatures lurking around.

"If I lost the chain and my light I'd be lost down here," he said. "Couldn't even tell which way was up because I couldn't see my bubbles. And right now I've got negative buoyancy.

"Negative buoyancy. That's a nice technical way of saying that I'd sink. So the thing to do if I did lose my light and the chain would be to go in the opposite direction from sinking. Only how would you know which way that was, in the darkness?

"The thing to do would be to drop my weight belt and come on up and throw away my lung and my inhalator and my suit and never go diving again, amen. Diving is a very nice sport in the daylight, in midsummer, when you're in forty feet of water and can see all the pretty rocks and pretty fishes. But at night in twenty fathoms, diving is for idiots.

"Ought to be getting near the bottom now. Better get head first again so I can see what's down there. That is assuming that there's anything down there. At least I can look at the chain and my hands. It will be a comfort even

[36]

to see my own hands. I never knew I was so fond of them."

He upended again and the links of the chain swung into view. His faceplate was now pressed very firmly against his nose so he knew he was deep. He glanced at the Fathometer on his wrist. It showed ninety feet. The water was frigid. His face felt like a block of marble and he had no feeling in his hands. He went on down, seven links at a time.

Tom found the plane by the simple process of bumping into it. He hit it with his shoulder, froze on the chain, and turned laboriously in the direction of what had struck him. In the narrow beam of his headlight he saw some fuselage and after a while reasoned that he had bumped into the tail section of the plane which was sticking up from the bottom.

Buzzie swam into his flashlight beam. He had left the chain, having sighted the fuselage when Tom bumped into it. He had his head very close to the fuselage and was swimming along it, feeling his way with his hands. Tom joined him, swimming beside Buzzie so that they had the benefit of both their lights. The water was so cloudy around the wreck that there were no clear outlines and the light did not penetrate far. They had to explore with their faceplates inches from the fuselage, going forward to the pilot's compartment.

Suddenly they came to the end of the fuselage. There was a torn jagged edge from which the bent members of the airframe thrust up like so many branches of a bare tree. The plane was in at least two parts then. This was the tail section. The wing section with the pilot's and passenger's compartment was somewhere else, nearby, but utterly lost in the blackness of the deeps.

[37]

The only thing to do was to look for it. But first Tom swam to the open jagged end of the tail section and peered inside. It was just possible that the attaché case they were seeking might be there. He saw only the tortured airframe members and several wires twisted in a tangle.

He ducked out of the tail section again and located Buzzie, who was holding on to one of the pieces of twisted aluminum. Tom took a length of rope from his weight belt and tied one end securely to the tail section. Buzzie understood what was planned. The two of them would string out on the rope and start searching the immediate neighborhood for the rest of the plane. With the rope they could get back to the tail section and also the chain which would guide them to the surface. It wasn't strictly necessary to get back to the surface by the chain but it would be better to do so, since they would be close to the cutter which could pick them up in a hurry if anything went wrong.

The rope was twenty feet long. Tom went to the end of it and Buzzie took it in the center. When they were in position they started swimming slowly in a wide arc around the fuselage. It was difficult and dangerous work because of the reefs on the bottom. They had to go very slowly to avoid the reefs, but when they had completed the first sweep, they had not found the wing section.

They joined each other at the fuselage and Tom consulted his pressure gauge, measuring the amount of air left in his lung. The pressure was down to eight hundred pounds. There was enough for another fifteen minutes on the bottom. After that they would have to turn on their reserves and surface immediately. But now they must leave the tail section. Tom undid the rope, coiled it up, all but six feet, and gave one end to Buzzie. He glanced at the compass which was incorporated in his Fathometer and

[38]

set out parallel with Buzzie and headed on a northerly course. They would have to make successive sweeps over the bottom for as long as they could in the hope that in the time left, they could locate the passenger's compartment of the plane.

V.

BUZZIE WAS the first to sight the forward section of the plane. He soared over a jagged edge of reef, his flashlight showing the lovely golds and soft greens and purples of the seagrowth, and found, beyond the top, a submarine valley perhaps ten feet deep. He turned his light into it and spotted a shining object which at first he took to be a perch. Fish showed up like gleaming stars under water in the beam of the flashlight. But this "perch" did not move away, and so pulling gently on the rope to direct Tom's attention, he swam toward the bright spot in the water. It was the wingtip of the plane. He grabbed the edge and pulled himself along toward the fuselage. Tom joined him and they found the cockpit. As they had anticipated, it was jammed shut, but they could see the two figures inside. The pilot was slumped forward so only the back of his head was visible, and the passenger's head was thrown back so that he seemed to be looking with longing up to the surface.

Tom fumbled with the catch on the outside of the cockpit cowling, but the cockpit had been locked from the inside and nothing could be done to open it. He flashed his light along the fuselage and noted that the door was sprung. There was just enough of the edge of the door bent out to get his fingers under. He heaved as hard as he could, but without reward. Buzzie motioned Tom aside and started to attack the door with his shark billie. He succeeded in bending it back enough to be able to slip his hand in and get at the inside lock. He fumbled until he got the lock undone and the door came open, though only grudgingly because it was bent out of shape. A mass of bubbles exploded from the cockpit. The inflowing water, replacing the escaping air, set up a current that sucked Buzzie head first into the cockpit across the lap of the passenger.

His instinct was to back out, but instead he reached up to the top of the cockpit cowling, found the latch, and undid it. Tom, who had been watching him, swam up over the top of the cowling, pulled it back, and there was another explosion of bubbles from escaping air.

Pilot and passenger were seated side by side in the plane and Buzzie was busy with the passenger, feeling for the attaché case which should be beside him. Tom had his light on Buzzie and noted a brown fluid clouding the water.

Blood!

Blood meant sharks. Sharks could scent blood from a great distance, and they were especially active at night. He took his flashlight off Buzzie for a moment and made a quick sweep of the area of the ocean around.

Apart from the gleaming silver light of a few fish he

[41]

saw nothing. He put the light back on Buzzie again, who was having some difficulty. He had found the snake-link chain but the dead passenger was sitting on the attaché case. The only thing to do was to lift him up, and Tom reached down, took him by the shoulders, and tried to raise him off the seat. He was a heavy-set man and could not be readily lifted. Then Tom remembered that he was probably fastened in with a safety belt.

Buzzie had remembered this, too, and was fumbling with the release of the belt when there was a flurry in the water over them and something hit the wreck of the plane so hard that the two of them were thrust aside by the impact and Buzzie was knocked out of the cockpit.

A dull white shape passed through the beam of Tom's flashlight, no more than a few feet from him. Tom saw the moonshaped mouth with its rows of teeth, and then it was gone. A shark! And where there was one there would soon be a dozen!

He turned his light on Buzzie and saw to his horror a strong stream of air bubbles coming up from the intake hose of Buzzie's regulator. When the shark made its first pass, knocking Buzzie out of the cockpit, his intake hose had ripped on a piece of jagged metal. Buzzie had pulled his mouthpiece out of his mouth and clasped his hand over it. He had taken in a mouthful of water under pressure and was gagging on it.

Tom grabbed him by the shoulders, took his own mouthpiece out and thrust it at Buzzie. Buzzie was still gagging, with his hands over his mouth, conscious that he must not draw in or he would get water in his lungs.

He seemed panicked and ignored Tom's mouthpiece from which bubbles of air were now streaming. Tom got under Buzzie, pulled his hand away from his mouth, and jammed the mouthpiece between his lips. He began to feel a constriction in his own lungs due to lack of air. But they could still get to the top by buddy-breathing if only Buzzie wouldn't panic. Tom swallowed to ease the constriction in his lungs and felt a moment's relief. Buzzie was gagging into the mouthpiece but he held it between his lips. "Gag and be hanged to you, but suck some air," Tom said fiercely to himself. "Go on. Suck some air. And give it back to me. Do you suppose I can hold my breath forever?"

At last Buzzie managed to get a good breath of air in his lungs and gave the mouthpiece back to Tom. But he immediately gagged again, coughing out the air he had just received. Tom took one breath and stuffed the mouthpiece back between Buzzie's teeth. They were so close together that their faceplates were within a foot of each other and he could see Buzzie's face clearly.

His eyes were staring and he was trying to fight free of Tom, in a panic.

Drowning men often try to fight free of their rescuers, feeling that they are being held under water by them. Something was needed to calm Buzzie down, to give him a chance to get hold of his nerves and his courage.

Tom put his thumb and forefinger together and thrust them before Buzzie's faceplate. He was rewarded by seeing Buzzie relax. This was a standing under-water joke between the two of them. The thumb and forefinger together signified that Tom wanted a cigarette. When they had first gone diving together, Tom had been constantly patting himself on his chest and thighs. When they got to the surface Buzzie had asked him why he had been patting himself.

"I forgot where I was and was looking for my cigarettes," Tom had replied. And so the gag had arisen.

Tom's gesture introduced a touch of normalcy to the situation. It took Buzzie's mind off their danger and his panic went. He handed the mouthpiece back to Tom, whose lungs were by now bursting. Tom breathed in hard, but didn't get much air. His tank was almost exhausted.

He reached behind him, felt for the reserve supply lever, and pulled it down. Then he gave the mouthpiece back and fumbled for Buzzie's weight belt. They'd better surface in a hurry. He found the release strap, got a good hold of Buzzie and indicated that he was going to drop Buzzie's weight belt. Buzzie nodded and grabbed Tom by the shoulders. If his weight belt were dropped he would go soaring to the top away from Tom and the air supply unless he took a firm hold on his buddy. Tom pulled the strap and Buzzie's weight belt slipped off, headed for the bottom. The two of them, locked together with Buzzie higher than Tom, started moving more rapidly to the surface.

They would have to be careful now, surfacing so fast, to get the air out of their lungs quickly, so they could not be ruptured by the pressure. The thing to do was to take in only what was needed and breathe out deeply. In their anxiety they had forgotten about the sharks.

Meanwhile, on the surface, a dinghy had been lowered to follow the two divers' air bubbles as Tom and Buzzie moved along the bottom looking for the forward portion of the wrecked plane.

Two coastguardmen manned the dinghy, and Chuck was up forward with a portable searchlight, watching the bubbles and directing the boat. He had been given this position because it was assumed he was in some way connected with the lifeguards. In any case, he was Tom's friend and

[44]

that seemed justification enough. The bubbles were readily seen and when they stopped moving and came steadily from one spot, Chuck concluded that the two divers had found what they were looking for.

"I hope so," said Captain Williams who was also in the dinghy. "They've got about ten minutes air supply left."

Suddenly there was a big burst of bubbles on the surface. Chuck didn't know what to make of them.

"Probably opened the cockpit of the plane," said Captain Williams. "Should be back up any minute now." He seemed nervous, though Chuck could not imagine why. The dive seemed to be perfectly normal. He concluded that Captain Williams was always nervous when his men were on a body recovery or salvage job.

Captain Williams had taken a rifle with him in the dinghy and had volunteered no reason for this. He sat in the stern with it across his knees looking around at the dark surface of the ocean. Suddenly he spotted what he was looking for—a dark triangle of fin that made a quick wake through the water and then submerged.

"Sharks," he said grimly. "I knew they wouldn't be long coming. Can you see the bubbles clearly?"

"Yes," said Chuck. "They're coming up pretty steadily."

"Coming up in bursts, I suppose," said the captain.

"Well, they were," said Chuck. "But now there are bubbles coming up all the time and some in bursts."

"Cripes," said the Captain, "someone's in trouble down there."

He cupped his hands and hailed the cutter. "Bring her over here," he shouted, "and stand by to pick up the divers." The cutter glided over to them.

"I think someone's got a burst air hose down there,"

[45]

said Captain Williams. "And there're sharks around. Don't let anyone start shooting at sharks from on board. They may hit one of my men. I can handle them."

"As you wish," said a voice from the cutter.

The cutter's searchlights were now playing on the area where the bubbles were bursting on the surface. Chuck tried to see down in the water, but the light seemed to penetrate only an inch or two below the surface. Captain Williams transferred from the dinghy to the cutter and stood there with his rifle ready. Suddenly there was a heavy swirl in the water and a big fin showed up in the area illuminated by the searchlights. Captain Williams fired and a little spurt of water leaped up close to the fin. He fired again and the shark was gone into the darkness.

"Think you hit him?" someone asked.

"Maybe. Scared him anyway," was the reply.

A fish leaped out of the water in the illuminated area, followed by two more, and then another shark fin cut a swift line across the surface. Captain Williams fired again but this time he was sure he had missed.

"Can you still see those bubbles?" he shouted to Chuck.

"Yes," said Chuck. "But there're not many of them. They're coming up in bursts but there's a longer wait between them."

"Buddy breathing," said Captain Williams with some satisfaction. "They ought to be here any second now. There they are! Over at the edge of the light!"

A black, barely visible shape had broken the surface. The searchlights were shifted to it immediately and picked up the hooded head of Buzzie and the silver torpedo shape of his tank. Tom's head broke the surface almost immediately afterward. Then, as the cutter moved toward the two men, a shark sped out of the darkness

[46]

toward them. Captain Williams fired twice in quick succession, but the shark kept coming. The dorsal fin was only six feet from Buzzie, who was nearest to the shark. He turned in the water to face it, and then Tom submerged going toward the shark. There was a swirl on the surface, and a white foam spread over the water. Cutter and dinghy had reached the spot, and Buzzie was hauled aboard the cutter.

Then Tom's head appeared, and Chuck reached out and grabbed him by the shoulders. Exerting all his strength, he hauled Tom into the dinghy. His legs were hardly clear of the water before another shark came in and turned over on its back to make a pass at Tom's feet. Captain Williams fired into its white belly.

Tom lay gasping for breath in the bottom of the boat. He was still unable to speak when he was transferred to the cutter and Captain Williams and Chuck started to take the wetsuits off the two men, after getting them below. Buzzie still had his tank on his back, though a rip in his air hose told what had happened to him on the bottom.

"Didn't get the attaché case," said Tom, when he was at last able to speak. "There was some blood and the sharks came in. Buzzie ripped his air hose on the bottom and we had to buddy-breathe back up. Is Buzzie O.K.?"

"Sure," said Captain Williams. "He's over in the other bunk. And he did get the attaché case."

"He did!" said Tom, surprised.

"Yeah. He had just tied it on the webbing of his tank when the shark hit. That's why he didn't drop his tank when you were surfacing."

Tom sat up in the bunk and looked over at Buzzie who was beginning to recover in the other one.

"Hey! Buzzie!" he shouted.

[47]

"Yeah," said Buzzie.

"You got any cigarettes?"

"Sure," said Buzzie, "in the pocket of my wetsuit."

The two started laughing, and nobody understood what they were laughing about.

VI.

THE BATTLE with the sharks filled Chuck with a deep fear of the ocean. It was a new experience for him. Whatever his troubles had been in the past, he had always found great consolation in the ocean. Even looking at it, broad and strong and enduring, gave him a sense of peace. Inclined to loneliness by nature, for he did not like group activities and had no special friends, the ocean had become for him a soothing companion, and it was for this reason that he spent most of his spare time on the beach, sometimes surfing, sometimes just looking for semiprecious stones, sometimes just looking at the great expanse of water. But now he knew there were horrors in the ocean. He had of course known there were sharks in the Pacific but had regarded them as remote creatures, far, far out in the deeps. The sight of the shark pack swirling around

Tom and Buzzie changed this. The ocean was not a friend but a place of menace, and he became afraid of it.

One immediate result was that he found excuses for not continuing his instructions in scuba diving under Tom. When Tom called up to suggest another lesson, Chuck put him off. He had a lot of homework to do, he said, and couldn't go away. He did indeed have homework, but no more than the usual amount. The truth was he didn't want to study scuba diving any more. It was all right in a swimming pool. Nothing dangerous could happen there. But after the pool instruction the day would come when he must go down in the ocean. And the very thought of it now filled him with fright, though previously he had longed for such an adventure.

"I don't think I'm ever going to understand that boy," his father said to his mother one day. "He doesn't play football, basketball, or baseball. He's always off mooning by himself. He hasn't even got a girl friend as far as I know. When I was his age—"

"When you were his age you were scared stiff of girl friends," said Mrs. Crawford. "I know. I lived right next door to you and if I said 'Hi' to you in the street, you blushed like a fire truck."

Mr. Crawford grunted. He had to admit that at Chuck's age he was painfully shy with girls. As a matter of fact, to this day he didn't feel entirely comfortable in the presence of women. It was all right if his wife was there, but left alone with a visitor on his hands for a few minutes, he could find nothing to say.

"Never mind about you and me," he grunted. "We're talking about Chuck. There are whole days when he hardly says a word to me. If I ask him how he's doing at school, he says 'All right, I guess.' If I ask him how he's feeling,

[50]

he says 'All right, I guess.' That's the only answer he ever seems to make. If he didn't know how to say 'All right, I guess,' he'd be a mute.''

"Three years ago you were complaining because he said everything was 'neat','' replied Mrs. Crawford with a smile. "It's just the way everybody his age has of talking.''

"It seems to me that youngsters these days need only a few phrases to get by, and the whole of the English language is wasted on them. Maybe the thing to do is teach them five or six phrases and then send them out to work. I don't think they've got any sensitivity. When I was a boy—''

"When you were a boy all you ever said about anything was that it was 'swell',' said Mrs. Crawford. "Don't worry about Chuck. He's a little different, it's true. But everybody can't be the same. And trying to make him act like everybody else only makes him retreat further into himself.''

"I'll tell you what's the matter with him,'' said Mr. Crawford, with some heat. "He lacks aggressiveness. He won't play football because he isn't aggressive and the same goes for baseball and basketball and any other kind of game. He hasn't any guts. He's got no faith in himself. He's afraid he can't win and so he won't try. That's what's the trouble with him. And I'm going to talk to him about it.''

Mrs. Crawford said nothing. She was afraid that her husband might do more harm than good in his talk with their son. Chuck might just clam up and resent it. But fathers were supposed to talk to their sons and she sensed that there was a relationship here in which she was incompetent to interfere.

[51]

Mr. Crawford was, if anything, a man of his word. Once he had made up his mind to do something, he never delayed. Nor did he seek out any smooth, oblique approaches, but tackled each problem as it arose, head on. When Chuck came back from school that day he found his father at home instead of down at the paint store. He had decided that the paint store could wait while he tackled his son.

"I want to talk to you, Chuck," he said, and led him into the den that served as a study.

Chuck was immediately filled with dismay and wondered what he had done wrong now. He realized that little that he did met with his father's approval. A vague sense of parental disapproval formed an uneasy background to his days.

"There's something the matter with you, Chuck," said his father when he had closed the door of the den, "and we're not getting out of here until I've found out what it is. Now. Is there something worrying you?"

"No," said Chuck.

"You feel good—you're not ill?"

"No."

"Then why in thunder do you spend your time mooning around in your room, reading or looking at your rocks, or down on the beach, and never go around with other kids your own age? Why don't you try out for the basketball team at the high school? You've got the height and the reach. You'd make a good basketball player."

"I don't like basketball," said Chuck.

"How do you know you don't like it if you've never played it?" demanded his father.

"I don't know," said Chuck. "I just don't like it."

"Well, it isn't healthy to be just by yourself all the

[52]

time. You've got to learn to mix with others. You'll never make a success unless you learn that. To be successful, you've got to belong.''

''You think you're successful?'' said Chuck. The words came out of him without any plan on his part. It was as if he had been hit a blow and he had struck back. And his father's talk of ''belonging'' and being a ''success'' was a blow to him.

''Sure I figure I'm a success,'' said Mr. Crawford. ''I own this house. I have about six thousand dollars of my own money in the bank and save two hundred a month. I own a paint store. I've been president of the Chamber of Commerce here three years in succession. And I started with nothing and no one to help me. That's success.''

Well, said Chuck to himself, it may be success to you but it isn't to me. It's very ordinary. Nothing at all. Nothing to spend the whole of your life working for. Nothing to put all your thought and your energy into—just to own a house and a paint store and be president of a chamber of commerce in a little town nobody ever heard of.

But he couldn't tell his father this, because it would hurt him too much, so he kept quiet. He wondered if that was what was ahead of him too—a paint store and a house and whatever kind of prestige went into being president of a chamber of commerce in a town of twenty thousand people—a fifth-rate city to give it its proper classification.

Mr. Crawford, having got onto the subject of himself, was not to be cut off by his son's silence. He didn't know what was going on in the boy's mind, but believed that a discussion of how he had achieved his present position would do his son good.

''You've got to be aggressive, Chuck,'' he said. ''That's what does it. You've got to have courage. You've got to believe in yourself. Now when I started that paint store I went into debt for twelve hundred dollars and I didn't have twelve hundred nickels. And there was a ten-thousand-dollar mortgage on this house. But I figured people needed paint and I was the man to sell it to them. And I was right. Guts. That's what it takes. Self-confidence. And it seems to me that self-confidence is one thing that you haven't got. Now you listen to me, boy. You don't get self-confidence over night. You get it by degrees. You get it by trying things and failing and trying again until you have some idea of what you can do and what you can't do. And a good way to build up self-confidence is to play games. For if you don't learn to trust yourself, nobody else is going to trust you. That's for sure.''

Chuck was listening with only half an ear. All this sounded vaguely familiar. He'd heard it from others before. The teachers talked about it at school and it was inherent in the stories he read. But it was just a formula that didn't apply to him and his problems. Because inside there was an unknown world that even he hadn't explored and others didn't guess at. It was a world full of longings and full of fears, full of bursts of confidence and agonies of self-doubt. How could he explain such a world to anyone? He couldn't even explain it to himself. It was something that had to be experienced and only he could experience it. So it was beyond explanation or transfer into someone else's consciousness.

The only person who seemed to have an instinctive inkling of his troubles was Tom. He would like to be a close friend of Tom's because he seemed to understand him. But he couldn't now—because of his fears. Tom wouldn't understand that he didn't want to learn more about scuba diving because of the sharks. If he told him, Tom would

[54]

call him a coward—which was what he was. His father thought him gutless and Tom would think him a coward. He was more alone and mixed up than ever.

His father was still talking. "There's a basketball game at the high school auditorium tonight," he was saying. "You and I are going. I don't care whether or not you want to go. We're going. Something has to be done to awaken your interest in the world around you and get you in there pitching."

"O.K.," said Chuck.

"Don't you want to go?" asked his father, almost pathetically.

Chuck shrugged. He didn't care who beat whom at basketball. It was without importance to him. He'd sooner be alone somewhere.

"I just can't figure you out," said his father and left. Chuck went to his own room and lay down across his bed staring at the ceiling. After a while he turned to look at the contents of the room. He had kept all the things he had had as a kid and looked at them now with a sense of detachment.

There was a pair of roller skates and a bunboard and a model of the Bounty and a warped tennis racket. There was a toy bulldozer that ran off a battery and hadn't worked for years, and an old flashlight, and pictures he'd done in crayon of an Indian in a canoe. They had all been his once, but they did not seem so now. They seemed to belong to someone he had known—some kid that he'd known and been fond of and had parted company with. The kid had gone off somewhere, leaving these toys behind, and Chuck had only an academic interest in them.

He got up and picked up one of the roller skates. It had been a great treasure years ago. For a second he felt an echo of the excitement he had experienced when his father had given him the roller skates on his seventh birthday. But then the feeling went and he put the skate down. It was just as if the boy he had been then had died and someone else had been born in his place and he was that person.

There was a knock on the door and his mother came in.

"Tom's on the phone," she said. "He wants to know whether you'll come over to his house and take another lesson in scuba diving."

To her surprise, Chuck sat down on his bed and put his head between his hands but made no reply.

"I'll tell him you're busy," she said and went out. She was back in a minute.

"He says maybe you can make it tomorrow," and sat down beside him. "What is it, Chuck?" she asked quietly. "Isn't it something you can tell me?"

"It's nothing," said Chuck. "Just leave me alone."

He went to the basketball game with his father that night and was thoroughly bored. His father, though a member of the audience, seemed to play the whole game and kept up a running critique of the players, telling them when to pass, and to try a floor shot, and when to shoot. After the game Mr. Crawford had a talk with the coach and they both agreed that the high school needed more practice in offense. They had lost, 32 to 24.

"Swell game," said Mr. Crawford on the way home. "When I was a boy . . ."

But Chuck didn't listen. He was wondering what he was going to say to Tom the next time he called to offer him some lessons in scuba.

VII.

TWO DAYS LATER Tom Prior called at Chuck's house. When Mrs. Crawford opened the door she found him standing on the doorstep with two big lobsters held in his stubby hands.

"Hope you like lobster, Mrs. Crawford," he said. "I got 'em a couple of hours ago diving off the harbor."

"Goodness, are they alive?" asked Mrs. Crawford.

"Sure are," said Tom. "If you've already fixed dinner, put 'em in the freezer. They're real good." He motioned to give the lobsters to Mrs. Crawford, who drew back in fright.

"You put them in the freezer yourself, Tom Prior," she said. "I daren't touch them while they're alive." She led the way into the kitchen.

"Where's Chuck?" asked Tom when they had returned to the living room.

"In his room. I'll get him," said Mrs. Crawford. She called Chuck, who appeared with some reluctance because of all the excuses he had been making to Tom. But Tom, though by now he knew that Chuck had been giving false reasons for not wanting to go on with his scuba diving, showed no hard feelings.

"Just brought a couple of lobsters," he said. "And don't give me any stuff about homework to do tonight. I want you to come round to the house ready for some more diving lessons. So don't eat much dinner."

"I've been thinking about this diving business," said Chuck, trying to sound casual, "and I've decided to give it up. I haven't got the time and I haven't any gear and so on."

"Tell that to the Marines," said Tom. "*I* was in the Navy. Be there about eight and if you aren't I'm going to come around and get you myself. Got someone I want you to meet anyway. About your age."

As if that matters, said Chuck to himself. But aloud he said, "O.K. I'll be there. But I'm not going to do any diving. Just a waste of time for me."

"Look at those lobsters I just caught and then see if it's still a waste of time," said Tom and left.

"I think you ought to have shown Tom a little more enthusiasm," said his mother when the door had closed. "He's going out of his way to be friendly."

"He's going out of his way to get me to do something that he wants me to do and I don't," snapped Chuck. "That's usually the case," he added. Then he felt miserable about saying such a thing.

When he arrived at Tom's house, he found Tom alone. He was in the living room working at a table on which he

[58]

had a number of seashells he was mounting carefully on a board.

"Mary's out with Shirley," he said. "Shirley's my niece. I want you to meet her. She's spending a couple of months with us. They'll be back in half an hour."

He got up from the table and selected a pipe from perhaps a dozen that littered the mantlepiece. Though Chuck had been in this room several times before, he noticed for the first time how much it was linked with the sea. Apart from the seashells, there was an old anchor in one corner, a big stuffed sea bass over the fireplace, and a rack containing a number of underwater weapons—Hawaiian slings, arbalettes, and so on. A bookcase held many books about the sea, ranging from Nordhoff and Hall's *Mutiny on the Bounty* to Potter's *Treasure Divers of Vigo Bay*. And to complete the effect there was a big picture of a windy expanse of ocean on the wall opposite the fireplace. Tom filled his pipe, lit it, and turned toward Chuck, but looked past him as was his way. "Those sharks scared the daylights out of you, didn't they?"

"Yeah," said Chuck, all his defenses down, "they did."

"And that's why you don't want to do any more scuba work?"

"I guess so."

"Glad to hear it," said Tom quietly. "I thought maybe you didn't like scuba diving. If it's just the sharks, there's nothing to it. They scared me, too. In fact for the next couple of nights I kept dreaming about them. I dreamed the first night that I was caught down there in that plane and the sharks were taking big bites out of me like a kid eating an apple."

"Well, with that many sharks down in the ocean, I don't

[59]

want any part of diving,'' said Chuck, relieved now that he had brought his fear out and had confessed it plainly.

"I guess I shouldn't have let you come along on that trip,'' said Tom. "I didn't think it was going to be that bad. It's like taking someone out for his first drive in an automobile and winding up in a head-on collision. The odds are thousands to one. Still the chance is there, and if someone's first automobile ride wound up in a crash, he wouldn't want to get into an automobile again for a long, long time—if ever.

"It would be a pity if you let this interfere with your plans to learn scuba. There's a wonderful world under the ocean to be explored and lots of things in it besides sharks.''

"Maybe,'' said Chuck, "but if I came up against a shark down there, I'd just panic and drown myself.''

"I doubt it,'' said Tom. "I've seen lots of them. Normally they don't bother you at all. In fact, most of the time they're more wary of you than you are of them. They even get scared by air bubbles. Lots of guys have frightened sharks off by just breathing hard and letting a lot of bubbles out.

"Here's something you ought to think about, Chuck. There are all kinds of dangers in life. Life isn't safe anywhere, even in your own home. You've got to learn to accept danger as a part of living. Otherwise you can wind up a nervous wreck. One of the great things about scuba diving is that it teaches you to accept danger and cope with it. Don't kid yourself. When you get down under the water with just a lung and a regulator to keep you alive, it's dangerous. But something happens to you as a result of accepting this danger, deliberately going into it, that is well worth while.

[60]

"Kids don't recognize danger. They have no judgment and no experience. People have to tell them what danger is—train them not to ride their bikes in the middle of the street and so on. When you start to recognize danger, you begin to grow up. When you start to learn to meet and handle danger, you start becoming a man.

"Right now you're kind of lost. I know. You're not a kid any more and you're not a man either. And you're too much alone for your own good. Why don't you give yourself a challenge instead of trying to figure everything out? Make up your mind that you're going to become expert with scuba and go on down in the ocean and get lobsters and fish and see what is there. Other people do it. Thousands of them. What's the matter with you? You going to say they've got more guts than you have?"

"The first time I talked about scuba diving, you gave me a long lecture on how dangerous it was and how a lot of people drowned through not knowing how to handle their equipment," said Chuck. "Now you're giving me a pep talk to get me to do something you say yourself is dangerous. Doesn't make sense."

"It makes sense and you know it," said Tom. "I'm asking you to do something that will help you to grow up. If you hadn't any interest in the ocean, I wouldn't ask you. I'd advise you to take up hot-rodding or something else. Flying maybe. But you have a natural love of the ocean and you are a natural scuba diver. You got scared by the sharks. Are you going to admit that those sharks can keep you out of the ocean, that you're going to turn over the whole ocean to them and stay safely on land for the rest of your life? Are you going to admit there's something you are so scared of that it will confine your activities from now until the day you die?"

"I don't *have* to go scuba diving," said Chuck. "It isn't something I *have* to do, any more than I have to take up jumping out of airplanes with a parachute for a hobby. I can get along without it."

"I don't believe it," said Tom quietly.

"Don't believe what?"

"I don't believe you're that yellow. But if you are, you'd better not do any scuba diving. Because under water it's not only *your* own life that you have in your hands but your buddy's life as well."

"I don't think you've the right to say I'm yellow because I'm scared of sharks," said Chuck hotly. "Everybody's scared of sharks. It's natural."

"Sure is," said Tom. "Like I said, I'm scared of them myself. What's unnatural is letting the sharks run you right out of the ocean—keep you a prisoner on land. Once you do that almost anything you're scared of will start running your life. You'll find excuses for not doing things, saying that you really don't want to do them, when in fact you're scared. It isn't just scuba diving that's involved here but a whole big principle about how you're going to live for the rest of your life—"

At that moment the door opened and Tom's wife, Mary, came in with a stringy freckled-faced girl with sand-colored hair. They were both carrying parcels and the girl, who Chuck guessed was Shirley, put hers down in the middle of the living-room floor. Opening a big paper sack, she said, "Look what I bought. Special at two-fifty down at the Dive 'N Surf. Fits like a glove."

She took out a faceplate and handed it to Tom.

"And I got a pair of flippers, too," she said. "There's a sale on. The flippers aren't really a pair, but they are left and right foot and they fit me. One's blue though and the other's yellow." She produced the flippers.

[62]

"Shirley, I want you to meet Chuck Crawford," said Tom. The two looked each other over. Shirley saw a tall blond boy with hands too big for his arms and an aquiline nose that also seemed too big for his face. He was blushing. Chuck saw a girl he decided he wasn't going to like. She was dressed in toreador pants and her legs were as thin as pipe stems. She had blue eyes, which seemed bluer because of the red freckles all over her cheeks and forehead.

"Hi," said Chuck.

"Hi," said Shirley. Chuck didn't know whether to shake hands or not so he kept his hands in his pockets and felt all the more awkward. But Shirley didn't seem to notice. She was the talkative type and as soon as this brief introduction was over, she plunged right on about what was on her mind, which was skin diving.

"Is Tom going to teach you to use a lung, too?" she asked. The question was rhetorical, for she did not wait for a reply. "Gosh," she plunged on, "I can't wait. I've got to see if that faceplate really fits. I put it on and breathed in and not the tiniest bit of air leaked in. I think I can paint the yellow flipper blue or maybe the blue flipper yellow. That would make a pair of them. But it doesn't really matter. I mean the only things that will see that one is blue and the other is yellow are fish and who cares what fish think. Anyway they look nice in different colors. If I painted the yellow one blue, maybe it would come out green. Where can I change?"

Chuck was smiling despite himself at this flow of chatter.

"That room over there," said Mary, pointing, and Shirley was gone in a moment, leaving Chuck confused and feeling a little breathless as if it was he who had been doing all the talking.

[63]

"She's a bit overpowering at first," said Mary. "But she's a nice kid." Tom went off to change also, leaving Chuck alone with Mary.

"You don't do any skin diving?" Chuck asked, more to make conversation than to get information.

"No," said Mary, "I'm too scared. And anyway I don't swim well enough and I'm too lazy to learn." Tom returned in his swim shorts, carrying a lung and regulator. Shirley followed him immediately and looked at Chuck in surprise.

"Aren't you going to change?" she asked. "Don't tell me that I have to do this all by myself—the only victim. I need a fellow sufferer." Tom was checking the valve on the lung and looked up at Chuck. It was a direct, challenging look.

"O.K.," said Tom. "Now I want you to swim to the end in a second."

"Hurry up," said Shirley. "See you at the bottom of the pool." When he returned, Shirley was already diving for her face mask, putting it on underwater and clearing it. He threw his into the pool, dived after it, got it on and cleared it, and was grateful that he hadn't forgotten the technique.

"How much do you weigh?" Tom asked when he got to the side.

"A hundred and fifty pounds."

"Put this weight belt on," said Tom. "It weighs eight pounds. You should just about be able to float with it on. Check and see."

Chuck put on the weight belt and got into the pool. Out of water the belt felt enormously heavy. In the water, he did not feel the weight so much, but it dragged him down so that he had to work to remain on the surface.

"O.K.," said Tom. "Now I want you to swim to the end of the pool with that weight belt and back again. Go as fast as you can." The task seemed tremendous. Chuck found he had to use the breast stroke to keep his head up and get some air. Even so, he got several mouthfuls of water and choked a couple of times before he got back from the far end of the pool.

"Good," said Tom, "you're doing all right. But you don't have to take a breath with every stroke. Next time try taking one deep breath and then doing two or three strokes with your head down before you come up for air again. You can go faster that way. Shirley, you ready?"

"Yes," said Shirley, "but soaking wet, which is what I am now, I only weigh a hundred and five pounds, so don't sink me."

"We'll give you six pounds to try out with," said Tom. He removed some of the weights, substituted lighter ones, and the girl swam to the end of the pool and back with the weight belt around her waist. She was out of breath, too, on her return; but not too breathless to keep from talking.

"If the level of the pool has gone down," she said, "it's because I swallowed a lot of it. Golly, I thought I'd drown. If I stopped swimming for a moment I'd have drowned. I'm sure you put more than six pounds on that belt. There must be at least a ton. Maybe a ton and a half . . ."

"When you get your breath we'll start using the lungs," said Tom laughing. "Who wants to be first?"

"Me," said Shirley. And then she looked at Chuck and blushed and said, "Sorry. I'm always pushing myself. You take first and I'll just sit on the edge of the pool and hold my breath until it's my turn."

[65]

VIII.

TWO WEEKS LATER Chuck was ready for his first ocean descent. That is to say, he was technically ready for it, for he had received intensive instruction from Tom in the swimming pool.

He had learned never to hold his breath while under water because of the danger of injury to his lungs if he ascended even a few feet with compressed air in them. He had learned to take off his lung at the bottom of the pool and come up to the surface, breathing out all the way. He had learned to dive into the pool without a lung, swim under water to one lying on the bottom, take a breath from it, leave it, and swim to another, and so on along the length of the pool, the lungs on the bottom providing air stations, as it were, at which he could breathe.

He had learned to dive to the bottom of the pool and put on a lung that was lying there waiting for him. And he had learned to buddy-breathe, he and Shirley using the same lung and passing the mouthpiece from one to the other. This technique, using the older twin-hose regulator, required the person with the lung on his back to be below the person with whom the air was being shared. This prevented water entering the hose.

All these things he had learned, always with the talkative Shirley as his companion. When he thought about it, he realized that but for her he probably would not have gone through with the course. He had borrowed her courage—or been shamed into finding some of his own. There were times when he hated Shirley with her endless prattle. She took everything lightly, as if she hadn't a serious notion in her head, and had no idea what it was to be nervous or afraid. Certainly she never showed any fear but always seemed eager to get on to the next stage of the lessons. Tom had even lectured her on having some respect for diving.

"The ocean never forgives a mistake," he said. "Remember that. Have some respect for it."

Shirley nodded her head with great enthusiasm. "When do we go down?" she asked. "In the ocean, I mean."

That was how much regard she had for the hazards. The attitude made Chuck dislike her, yet he had a kind of fondness for her as well. Sometimes, in the middle of her prattle, he caught her watching him with a look that suggested she knew and understood the hidden fears in his own mind and would like to help him with them. That was a lot to get out of a look, and yet Chuck did.

Now they were ready to go down in the ocean. They had hired their equipment—lungs, regulators, wetsuits, weight belts—from Dive 'N Surf. They were allowed to rent it only because Tom assured the owner that he had

[67]

given instruction to the two of them and was going down with them himself.

They had planned to make their first dive inside the breakwater of King Harbor. But Shirley had begged to be allowed to go down outside. "Inside will be just like the swimming pool," she said. "And I've seen all I want of the bottom of swimming pools. Let's really go down in the ocean where we can see lots of fish and stuff. Maybe we can find some lobsters. Lobsters are my favorite food next to turkey. If I had a favorite dinner it would be lobster and turkey together and maybe some steak as well."

"I don't know how we got onto the subject of dinner when we were talking about diving," said Tom. "But we'll go down inside the harbor. You'll find it exciting enough. Later, if you do well with this, you can go down outside."

"How deep is it in the harbor?" asked Shirley.

"Twenty-five or thirty feet at the deepest point," said Tom. "Enough for you two."

So they took their first dive in the harbor behind the breakwater. The water was calm, which was one advantage, and they could wade in without having to battle their way through breaking surf. "You'll learn about entering through surf later," said Tom. "More divers get into trouble in surf a few yards off shore than far out to sea."

They changed in some booths used by the lifeguards and met on the shore by the water in their wetsuits. Tom checked the two of them to see that their gear was in order. He found Chuck had, in his anxiety, put his weight belt on first. The harness of the lung was over the weight belt.

"That's about as dangerous a thing as you can do, Chuck," said Tom seriously. "If you undid that weight

[68]

belt on the bottom to surface in a hurry, it wouldn't come off. It would hang up in the harness."

Chuck nodded. His lips felt dry, and he wasn't able to think clearly. He had to unbuckle the straps of his lung, take the weight belt off, buckle the straps up again, and then put on the weight belt once more. He was carrying twenty pounds, which felt enormously cumbersome and heavy. In his anxiety he forgot how to strap on the weight belt so that it would come free with one pull. His hands were trembling, and he hoped Shirley wouldn't notice this.

She, however, had problems of her own. In checking her equipment Tom found that she had hooked on her regulator upside down. It comforted Chuck that she had made a mistake, too, though he could not believe it was because she was nervous.

At last they were all ready. Chuck put his faceplate over his nose and eyes, and it immediately fogged up. He was angry over his own stupidity. He must first clean the faceplate out with saliva and then wash it with water to prevent the fogging. He took it off, lumbered a few steps into the water and spat in the faceplate. Shirley had already attended to this procedure, so they waited for Chuck. He wished they would both go away and leave him. If they went off and submerged, he could pretend there was something wrong with his regulator, go back ashore, and not have to dive. But they waited for him.

"O.K.," said Tom. "Put in your mouthpieces and see if you're getting air." Chuck did so. He put the mouthpiece in his mouth, breathed in, and was rewarded by a noisy rush of air. The air tasted rubbery and didn't seem good for breathing. He thought he wasn't getting enough of it either. He was still head and shoulders above the water and he breathed so hard his regulator made a prodigious noise, but there still didn't seem to be enough air to keep him alive if he were under water. He felt sick with anxiety.

"Everything all right?" asked Tom. "Let's go then. Stay close to me and if you lose sight of me, come up to the surface—slowly. Remember, don't go up faster than the smallest bubbles from your outlet valve."

Tom put his regulator in his mouth, turned, and dived easily forward below the surface. He was gone in a second and Shirley with him. For a horrified moment Chuck stood watching the place they had left and then dived himself, breathing at a tremendous rate.

He was conscious immediately of a tremendous isolation. It was as if, in one second, the whole world with all its noise and clamor had ceased to exist. He was surrounded by silence and supported by nothing. The silence was broken only by the noise of his own frantic breathing through his regulator. The sea around was the palest green. It was utterly still and utterly noiseless. He was still breathing hard, gasping for air, and it took a deliberate effort of will to slow his breathing down.

He peered ahead and caught in the vague vast greenness an indistinct glimpse of white. It seemed a long way ahead and much lower down. At first the sight of this frightened him and then he recognized the whiteness as Tom's lung and hurried to swim down to him.

He had learned in the pool to use his feet underwater and not his arms. But in his anxiety to be reunited with Tom he used his arms in a breast stroke, pulling himself down in the water, his heart beating so heavily he could feel the pulse in his neck. The water became a little colder on his face and hands, as if he were in a warm room and

[70]

someone had opened a door letting in a cold draft. As he went down, he felt a tremendous pain in his ears.

It came on suddenly and was so sharp that he could not bear it. Pressure. He must come up a foot or two and equalize the pressure in his eardrums by forcing air into the Eustachian tubes. Only because he had been trained by Tom did he know what to do. His reaction was based on that training, and he did not have to think. He stopped swimming down, felt himself rise a little in the water, placed his hand against his faceplate and pushed it hard against his face. Then he breathed hard through his nose into the faceplate. The pain in his ears lessened. He breathed into the faceplate again and experienced a slow rumbling noise in his inner ear. The pain was gone. He could continue on down.

He looked ahead but could find no sight of Tom or Shirley. They might have waited for me, he thought. They're supposed to wait for me. We're not supposed to get out of sight of each other.

The only thing to do was to swim in the direction in which he had last seen them. He continued down and forward, and saw in the deepened green, a brownish yellow, something weaving gently to and fro. Seaweed. He had been ridiculously frightened of it. He rose a little to go over the seaweed, still looking ahead for a glimpse of Tom's tank.

Suddenly something touched him on the leg. It was a soft, insidious touch, like a fat flabby hand, reaching for him in the dark. That was enough. He kicked vigorously and shot toward the surface, forgetting all about not overtaking the small air bubbles. His ears started to pop and suddenly Tom appeared before his faceplate, pointing vigorously to his air bubbles. Only then Chuck remem-

[71]

bered about not ascending fast enough to strain his lungs. He slowed down, letting himself drift up to the surface. It seemed to take forever to get there.

"What bugged you?" asked Tom when they got to the top.

"I couldn't find you," said Chuck. "Something touched me on the leg. I thought it might be a shark." He felt very silly making these excuses which sounded paltry now that they were up on the surface again. But Tom didn't scoff at him.

"I touched you," he said. "You were swimming around in circles on the bottom. You kick harder with your right leg and pull harder with your right arm. So you were making circles. I watched you for a while and then touched you to straighten you out. Sorry if I scared you."

"I couldn't find you," repeated Chuck.

"Just keep close," said Tom. "Come on. Shirley's still down there." He was gone in a second. This time Chuck dived immediately and was able to follow Tom to the bottom. But he followed him too closely and kept bumping into him. They located Shirley easily. When Tom surfaced, she had grabbed a lump of seaweed and just stayed with it. She had contrived to sit on the bottom, anchored to the seaweed, and waved to them as they came down.

There was a burst of bubbles, but not from her exhaust valve, and she started to choke and went rocketing up to the top herself. Tom grabbed her to slow her down, and she tried to fight away from him. They went to the top together and Chuck joined them. He didn't fancy waiting on the bottom until they returned. Shirley was gagging when she got to the surface and was very angry.

"Beast," she said to Tom. "I just won't ever talk to

[72]

you again. What do you mean trying to hold me down there when I was drowning?"

This all came out through splutters and tremendous efforts on Shirley's part to get her breath. Tom was laughing. "Look, kid," he said. "There's just one thing you can't do on the bottom of the ocean and that is talk. You opened your mouth to say something and you got it full of water."

"I forgot," said Shirley. "I saw a big old crab down there and I wanted to tell you about it."

"No talking," said Tom. "If you want to show me something, just point. Under water, pointing isn't considered impolite."

They went down again. It seemed to Chuck to take forever to get to the bottom. The water grew colder in layers, and Tom went down much faster than he. Chuck had to stop once to clear his ears, but at last they were together on the bottom of the harbor, and Tom, after glancing upward to locate the sun's position and get his direction, pointed to the right and they set off together.

Tom had a peculiar method of swimming under water. He kept his feet together and undulated his body, bending backward and forward at the waist. In this way he went forward smoothly and swiftly. Chuck was still using his arms, and still breathing hard, using up far too much air. His nerves relaxed watching Tom, and he tried swimming with his feet only. This required much less effort, and he actually went faster.

Gradually Chuck began to relax. He took his eyes off Tom for a moment and looked upward. He could see the surface as a glittering mirror far, far away. It was an entrancing sight. He flipped over on his back for a better

[73]

view but became giddy watching the stream of bubbles from his exhaust flowing up to the surface. It seemed that the bubbles were actually standing still and he was retreating from them, sinking lower and lower into the water. The giddiness persisted, and he turned face down again quickly to recover his balance.

Now he began to see colors that had escaped him before. The upper edges of the seaweed were a beautiful soft gold. Below they became a deep reddish-brown. The rocks were a royal purple in places and in others a vague blue. There were sharp dots of white on some, and occasionally a startling touch of red.

Tom held out a gloved hand to him. In it was some oval-shaped soft sea creature. The body was deep blue but around the edges was a fringe of gold. It was like a blue cushion with a border of golden tassels.

The sense of tension continued to leave Chuck slowly, and he breathed more easily, not gasping for each breath as if struggling for life. They came to a bare patch of sand and Tom pointed to two block dots on the bottom. He reached to the sand, dug into it a little distance behind the black dots, and came up with a crab that waved its legs and pincers in a slow, hopeless fashion.

Tom swam along with the crab in his hand and then pointed to an empty scallop shell on the bottom. He put the crab near it and the crab picked up the scallop shell in its claw. Tom grinned at Chuck. He would use the crab as a tool to pick things up with. It was a little underseas joke to be shared.

There was humor under the water as well as hazard. It was a good place to be, Chuck decided. He wasn't afraid any more.

IX.

THERE WERE two more dives inside the harbor before Tom decided to take Chuck and Shirley down in the rougher and deeper water outside the mole. Shirley was extremely anxious to do what she called some "real diving" and regarded the descents in the harbor as little more than an extension of what they had been doing in the swimming pool.

Chuck would have been content to continue in the harbor for a while. He didn't feel he was ready for deeper explorations. After their first descent, although they had remained down only an hour and had gone no deeper than thirty feet, he was exhausted. He went home and slept for four hours.

"An hour spent under water, the doctors say, is the equivalent of an hour spent running up and down a flight of stairs," said Tom. "You seem to be doing no work at all. Everything appears easy and effortless. Yet you are supporting enormous pressures on your body. Your leg and chest muscles are working against the resistance of dense water. It's very hard work all right. But you'll be surprised how quickly you adjust to it."

Chuck expected that with his second dive he would feel more at home. But he still had a moment of panic when he was completely submerged, and nightmare thoughts of his air supply getting cut off raced through his mind and had to be put aside deliberately. Although he enjoyed diving, he was uneasy the night before a descent, and slept badly. He thought of getting trapped under water or getting a cramp and being unable to swim ashore once he gained the surface. But sharks bothered him most and finally he broached the subject to Tom.

"Nobody knows much about sharks," said Tom. "Even marine biologists cannot tell you which sharks are dangerous and which are not. I've met sharks several times, and, if it is any comfort to you, they still scare me. But actually the shark menace is blown up out of all proportion. I don't know myself of a single case of a scuba diver ever being attacked by a shark on this coast. Plenty of us have seen sharks. None of us have been attacked by them. The theory is that they don't attack a swimmer who is completely submerged. If a swimmer is on the surface and a shark sees his feet or arms dangling down in the water, the shark may decide to attack. But that's a special case. And when you think of the millions of people who go swimming in the ocean every year and the infinitesimal proportion of them who have been attacked by sharks, it becomes plain that the shark menace is worse on paper than it is in the ocean."

"You say they don't attack scuba divers," said Chuck.

[76]

"But you and Buzzie were attacked by a whole flock of them when you were diving on the plane wreck."

"Right," said Tom, "but that was because there was blood around. Sharks seem to find their way mostly by scent. And they are drawn to any area where there is blood. If you cut yourself and start to bleed under water, the safe and sensible thing to do is to get out. The same thing is true about spearing fish. If you carry a catch of bleeding fish around under water, you are asking for trouble. You may get away with it time and again, but there may be a time when you don't and you're liable to be bitten by sharks and perhaps killed.

"The thing to do if you are fishing is work from a boat on the surface, and boat your catch just as soon as you can. Some people use a fish sling to keep their fish on. It is a wire contrivance that is put through the gills and the mouth of the fish and hung on the weight belt. I don't, because I think it is foolhardy to be under water with two or three bleeding fish around you. When I spear a sea bass or halibut, I keep it on the end of my spear until I get to the boat. That way, if a shark attacks, I can get rid of the fish in a hurry by just letting go the spear.

"Now the fact that I do that immediately suggests that the ocean is teeming with sharks and that just isn't so. Sharks prefer to stay in deep water and in my opinion it is a special occasion when they come in shore. But because any shark may be a potential killer, it is wise to take every possible precaution against them, like not keeping wounded fish around you under water, or diving in areas where a lot of garbage is dumped or is likely to be washed close to the shore by currents."

"Supposing I did meet a shark under water," insisted Chuck, "what should I do to protect myself?"

[77]

Tom shrugged. "What can I tell you?" he asked. "There's no reliable technique for dealing with sharks. Their snouts are supposed to be the only sensitive parts of their bodies. If Buzzie and I are diving in an area where we can expect sharks—on body recovery work, for instance—we use a shark billie, which is a baseball bat with one end studded with nails. Its main use is that you can, with luck, keep a shark at a distance from you. The nails stick in his hide and fend you off by the length of your arm and the billie. Buzzie once rapped a blue shark on the snout with his billie and it took off. There have been photographers who have bumped a shark on the snout with their cameras and he has retreated. That seems to prove they have sensitive noses.

"But beyond these few hints, I can't tell you much about dealing with sharks. As I've said, they don't teem in the ocean, they do not seem to bother scuba divers, and the main thing to do on sighting one is try not to panic and stay with your buddy. Even if you have a chance to get away yourself, stick with your buddy. Remember that. Always stick with your buddy. It's a basic rule of diving. Be as anxious about his safety as about your own."

"Killer whales are worse than sharks anyway, aren't they?" asked Shirley. "I've heard that they're so mean they'll knock people off rocks into the water to get at them and eat them. Or out of boats. They look kind of cute though. I mean the color. Sort of black and white in a nice pattern, like a panda bear. Of course I've never seen one but I've seen some pictures of them. A little killer whale must look real cute."

"Why did you bring up killer whales?" groaned Tom.

"Well, I thought if we were going to have a discussion

[78]

of the dangers of the deep, they ought to be given first place. They're the worst things in the ocean, aren't they?"

"The worst thing in the ocean is a big beast called panic," said Tom. "He's invisible, yet is constantly present and able to pounce at any moment, and usually when he's least expected. A sudden change of light releases him. Or the appearance of a big fish. Or someone touching you unexpectedly on the leg, particularly in strange waters. Or even swimming into a submarine current, or looking into a big cavern and having your tank catch on the top. Panic is the worst of the monsters of the deep and probably has more lives to his credit than any other monster down there.

"But killer whales are bad. In fact, very bad. If you see one, get out of the water as fast as you can. And if you can't get out of the water, find a nice cozy place to hide."

"You ever seen one?" asked Chuck.

"Yes," replied Tom quietly. "Diving with Buzzie off Monterey. You can't mistake them—they look about twice the size of a shark and are black and white. They are actually a form of dolphin though that's hard to believe, seeing how friendly dolphins are. Anyway, we saw one and the two of us got behind a reef quickly and stayed there until it was gone. Killer whales eat dolphin, seals, and certain whales. They are not as timid as sharks are supposed to be, but come right in to attack. And since a scuba diver may look like a dolphin or a seal to a killer whale, it is better to stay out of their way.

"But if one were to think of all the dangers there are in the ocean, no one would ever go diving. On the other hand,

[79]

if you were to think of the number of automobiles there are on the street and the prospect of being hit by one, few people would care to go out walking, let alone cross the road. The danger of attack under water by a shark or killer whale or a moray eel exists. But it is a remote danger and not sufficient to deter a man from diving.

"But watch for panic. That's the real killer. If you feel yourself getting scared out of your wits, force yourself to calm down and analyze the situation. Deliberately do nothing and analyze the cause of your fear. Once you can get your mind working rationally, you're halfway safe from whatever danger threatened you."

"What about whales?" asked Chuck.

"What about them?" echoed Tom.

"Well, there are a lot of California gray whales around at certain times of the year. Are they dangerous?"

"Not that I know of," said Tom. "Of course, I wouldn't want to get in a school of them, any more than I'd like to be caught in the middle of a highway with twenty-ton trucks buzzing all around me. There's a photographer up at the county museum who tells a story about getting into a jam with a whale. He wanted to make some movies of whales and went down near a pod—pod is the word for a flock of whales. He took some octopus down with him because whales like octopus, and he figured he could lure one or two whales near him.

"Things did not work out the way he planned, however. He sighted a whale with a baby close by, and that's a dangerous situation with any wild creature. The baby whale saw the octopus he was holding out, and came over to investigate. The baby swam round behind the photographer, and he was then between the baby and its mother.

"The octopus was no fool and knew the baby whale was

after him. So he kept swimming around the photographer with the baby whale after him. The octopus went down in front of the photographer and came up on the other side, slipping between his legs. And the little whale went around after him. They kept up this dodging game, using the photographer as a post for a while, and then the mother started to get mad.

"When a whale is placid you can hardly see its eyes. When it gets angry the eyes start opening up and the angrier the whale gets, the bigger the eyes get. The photographer told me that he glanced at the mother whale and her eyes were about as big as a dinner plate and getting bigger each second. She was sideways to him and turned head-on to charge. At that moment the baby whale caught the octopus, swallowed it, and went back to mother— thereby saving the photographer's life."

"Did the photographer get any pictures?" asked Shirley. "I'd say that if he'd got some pictures, he'd be so famous he'd probably never have to earn another penny in his life."

"No," said Tom, "he didn't get any pictures. And he's never gone down to photograph whales since."

"I'd have taken some pictures," said Shirley. "I mean there wasn't anything he could do to save himself anyway and so he might as well have taken pictures." Her attitude irritated Chuck.

"You don't know what you'd do," said Chuck. "It's all right to sit here and say you'd have used your camera. But you're not in any danger now."

"Well, what I mean is," said Shirley, not in the slightest degree offended, "if you're scared but helpless you might as well go ahead with what you set out to do. It would take your mind off being scared."

"Oh, baloney," snapped Chuck and Tom gave him a surprised look.

"Come on," he said quickly, "let's go diving."

Shirley blushed and bit her lip with vexation, though whether with Chuck or herself, it was hard to say.

X.

FROM THE Palos Verdes peninsula north to Malibu, a distance of something over thirty miles, the California coastline is sandy. It is ideal for swimming and surfing, but the absence of rocks and therefore of seaweed makes the fishing poor. To remedy this situation, to provide submarine structures on which algae and seaweeds might grow, thereby encouraging fish to collect and breed in the area, the Fish and Game Department hit upon a novel idea. They took a number of outdated trolley cars, banished from the downtown streets of Los Angeles, and dumped them in the ocean. They hoped that in a little while the trolley cars would become covered with algae and later with seaweed so fish would be encouraged to live and breed in and around them.

Tom had decided, as the first deep dive for Shirley and Chuck, to visit one of these trolley cars. It lay in a hundred

[83]

feet of water off the shore, the spot marked by a buoy floating on the surface and anchored to the trolley car below by a chain. Ideally it would have been better to go out to this buoy in a boat and dive from there. But no boat was available, and so the three had to proceed from the shore, battling through the surf until they got to the unbroken water where they could dive and swim below the surface toward the buoy. Once there, they would go down the chain to the car.

"Don't fight the surf going through," said Tom when they assembled at the water's edge. "Resist it but don't struggle. Hold on to your faceplate and go in backward through the breakers. Even though you are backing into them keep an eye on them. If a big one is coming, duck down and let it go over you. But remember to hold on to your faceplate. If that comes off you'll never find it again. All set?"

He didn't wait for a reply but walked into the ocean, spent a moment or two putting on his flippers, and then commenced backing out to the deeper water. Shirley joined him, but Chuck had some trouble getting his flippers on and the other two were well into the surf before he was ready for the attempt.

This irritated him. Tom was always preaching about staying with your buddy when diving. But he and Shirley took off whenever they were ready without seeing whether he, Chuck, was also ready. He got his flippers on after a struggle and started backing out into the surf. The task was made more difficult by the fact that there were a number of holes scooped out in the sand by riptides. He was constantly backing from water a foot deep into water three feet deep and then into shallow water again.

[84]

It was difficult, with his heavy lung on his back, his regulator strapped in place around his neck, and his faceplate on his forehead, to turn sufficiently to see behind him. He saw a big wave gather, its sides glittering like steel and rolling over relentlessly toward him. He took a deep breath and ducked as the wave broke with a seething explosion. It was only at the last moment that he remembered to clap his hand hard over his faceplate. In a second he was enveloped in a swirling mass of foam that sought to tear him off his feet and tumble him up on the beach. He dug his heels into the sand but the sand gave way under him. He was rolled on his side, struggled to get his feet on the bottom again, and finally surfaced, desperate for air.

Now the suck of the wave started to push him out to sea. Gasping hard through his open mouth, still with a hand pressed on his faceplate, he backed outward as fast as he could. His regulator, which was fastened with a strap around his neck, had been torn loose. It was dangling somewhere down beside him. He reached for it with his free hand, but there was not time to fasten the strap again.

Another comber broke, and again he was inundated and pushed around, and came up desperate for breath. He had dealt with only two combers, and he was beginning to feel tired already. Also he was frightened because he could not strap his regulator around his neck, and he knew that, being down in the water, it was probably leaking air. It was the one-hose type with the mechanism regulating the release of air in the mouthpiece rather than back on his tank.

He groped for the regulator, found it, and put it in his mouth just as a third breaker flung itself at him. This time he just went down to the bottom, breathing much harder

[85]

than was needed through the regulator because his fears were mounting. The surf was taking control of him, rather than he of himself.

When he came up again he found he was in a fairly calm area. He glanced quickly backward out to sea and saw a fourth wave building up. There was just a chance that if he dived to the bottom, using his regulator, and swam toward the wave, he would pass under it before it broke. He turned seaward, dived fast, and kicked hard with his feet. But since he still had his faceplate on his forehead he could not see where he was going. He opened his eyes for a second and found the visibility no greater than a few inches. There was a luminosity in front of him but he could see nothing.

Then he remembered something Tom had told him in the early days of his training. Think out everything you are to do before you get into the water, because things happen so fast you are not able to think clearly there.

He had certainly violated that precept. Still submerged, he slipped his faceplate into position. But it was full of water and gave him a sensation of choking. He didn't consider clearing it under water.

He came up, took off his faceplate, and caught a glimpse of Tom and Shirley beyond the breakers and halfway out to the buoy already. Another wave reared up between them. No time to fix his faceplate. He went down a few feet to get under it, and since he could travel faster under water than on the surface, remained down for thirty seconds, kicking hard to propel himself beyond the surf line.

When he came up again he was sufficiently far offshore to be clear of the surf. But he was still anxious, his nerves on edge and his body tense because of his battle in the surf. Little surface waves kept splashing over his face and he was aware that there was water in his mouth. Also he was breathing as hard as if he had been running at full pelt for some time.

"Stop breathing so hard," he told himself. "Calm down. Let's think this thing out."

These mental commands started his mind, which had been at the mercy of his emotions, working again. He deliberately breathed more slowly and the effect was wonderful. He could feel his nerves relax as if a net drawn tightly through the fibers of his body was cast loose.

He pulled his faceplate away from his face, tipped it, emptied the water out, and replaced it. It fogged up immediately. He had forgotten to prepare it against fogging by rubbing the inside of the glass with saliva and he did this now. Then he rinsed the faceplate out and put it on. He felt much better. He took a bearing on Shirley and Tom, submerged a few feet, and started swimming toward them.

Looking downward he saw the beautiful pale green of the ocean world, and far below, yet visible, the ashen sand looked like an inverted sky. Over it three small sting rays flapped forward, their wings undulating with quiet grace. The water got deeper, and the color changed from a pale to a darker green. The bottom disappeared. He seemed to be floating in nothingness, suspended in an infinite atmosphere of green in which there was no landmark to give him a bearing or a sense of distance.

He felt nauseated for a moment but fought this feeling off. It is all right, he told himself. This is perfectly normal. This is the ocean and I am in it and safe. All my equipment is working. There is no need for fear. He gradually began to enjoy himself, to luxuriate in the glorious freedom of being suspended in nothing, like a piece of thistledown floating a hundred miles above the surface of the earth. He would have liked to have gone down deeper, but wondered whether he was nearing Tom and the buoy. So he surfaced and saw Tom and Shirley only a few feet ahead of him clinging to it. He had joined them in a minute.

"Surf was a bit rough, eh?" said Tom.

"Yeah," replied Chuck.

"You did all right, though," said Tom. "I was watching you. Shirley and I found a little riptide and went out with it so we got through easily. But you did well. Held on to your faceplate and didn't choke. That's the main thing. Well, let's go down and look at the trolley car."

Chuck went first. He took hold of the chain, surface-dived, and started to pull himself toward the bottom on the chain. The angle of descent was very steep, almost perpendicular, and after a few seconds he became dizzy from the blood rushing into his head. Still he persevered. He could see the links of the chain sweeping in a gentle arc toward the bottom. But there was no bottom. It was represented by invisibility. The chain just disappeared into the profound nothingness that lay below him—a deep green gloom merging into utter invisibility.

After a while he felt a sharp pain in his ear, swallowed, and, pressing his faceplate against his face, breathed hard into it through his nose. The pain diminished but did not go entirely. He went down a few feet farther. The pain increased in intensity. He tried clearing his Eustachian tubes by swallowing and breathing into his faceplate through his nose, but the remedy was not sufficient.

He stopped on the chain and felt someone bump into his flippers. Slowly he upended himself so that his feet were pointed toward the bottom rather than his head. He could see Shirley and Tom above him, like two monstrous

[88]

growths clinging to the chain. He tried once more to clear his eardrums, but the pain from the unequal pressure remained. The air escaped from his faceplate when he exhaled into it through his nose and so he could not build up enough back pressure to clear his tubes.

Was this the limit to which he could dive? They could be down no more than forty feet. There was one further thing he could do—take off his faceplate, hold his nostrils, and blow air into them. But he was afraid to remove his faceplate. What if he could not clear it afterward? How terrible to be forty feet below the surface and not be able to see, not to have that comforting little cushion of air between his eyes and the water. But there was nothing for it. He could either stay where he was or remove his faceplate. If he went down any farther without equalizing the pressure, he would rupture his eardrums and that would mean the end of diving, perhaps for all time.

With a feeling of dread he pushed his faceplate up on his forehead, the air escaping from it in a burst of bubbles. The cold water, flooding around his nose and eyes, startled him. He opened his eyes, but Shirley and Tom had disappeared. He could hardly see the chain to which he was holding with one hand.

He took his nostrils between thumb and forefinger and blew hard through his nose. He was rewarded by a squeaking sound in his inner ear as his Eustachian tubes cleared, and immediately the pain was gone. He replaced his faceplate, turned on his left side, and looked up toward the surface. He put his hand on the right side of the faceplate, pressed it, and breathed through his nose into the faceplate. As the water was forced from it under the pressure of the air his sight returned. Tom was right opposite him, holding on to the chain. He was nodding his head vigor-

[89]

ously and held out his thumb and forefinger forming a circle as a gesture of approval.

Chuck started to feel wonderfully happy. He had done something he was frightened of doing without panic and efficiently. He was more of a master of himself and therefore of the underwater world. They continued downward.

Suddenly the water became intensely cold. Chuck could feel the shock of it through his wetsuit. For a moment he felt that his face and hands had been plunged into a snow bank. But his body adjusted to the shock very quickly. It's strange, he said to himself, how much cold my face and hands can endure. The water is frigid, and yet, now that the shock is over, my face and hands feel quite comfortable.

He looked down but could still see no sign of the trolley car. He could see five feet of the chain below him and then it melted, link by link, into nothingness. They continued to descend. Chuck was aware that the noise of his exhalation had changed in tone. Near the surface there was a hissing note. Deep down there was only a slight rumble.

Tom was wearing a two-hose regulator. No noise came from it that Chuck could hear. There were only bursts of beautiful silver bubbles, brighter than any jewel he had ever seen. These rose in a fairylike cloud toward the surface, increasing in size as they went upward. It was enchanting to watch them. There was something a little fearful, too, in the sight of the bubbles, for they were a reminder of something he was forgetting—that he was sixty or seventy feet deep in the ocean. He was now so much in possession of his nerves, that the thought he was actually under water came as quite a shock.

As he descended still farther the color around deepened from a pale green to the green of a thick glass bottle. And

[90]

then, going deeper and peering into the depths, he saw below him an area of subdued light. It was a gray light, with perhaps a ghost of yellow in it. Then, a few feet farther, he saw something roundish and dark below him. The outline of this dark shape was covered with a faint soft gold. Gradually he made out the shape of the trolley car. It was standing upright on its wheels on the sandy bottom and now came clearly into view.

It was utterly lonely and desolate—a pale dead shape in a pale dead world. He let go the chain and sank slowly down beside the trolley car, as gently as a leaf falling in the autumn to the ground. At this depth he had a slightly negative buoyancy. He could not float to the surface as he could have higher up. He and the trolley car were imprisoned by pressure on the bottom of the ocean.

With a slight flutter of his flippers he glided rather than swam to the side of the trolley. The concertina doors in front were in place, opening and closing gently in a submarine tide. It was as if all the people who had at one time used this trolley car and since died were still getting in and out of it.

The sight made him shudder. He was happy to turn and see Tom and Shirley behind him.

XI.

THERE WAS much more light on the ocean floor than there had been halfway down, and gliding along past the trolley, Chuck had the feeling that he was in a huge hall, whose vast roof was fifteen feet above his head, and whose walls encompassed him but could not be seen because they lay a great distance off.

The feeling that he was in such a place arose partially from the greater visibility on the ocean floor and partially because he was breathing very easily. It seemed then that this submarine hall was filled with air and he had had to struggle down to it through the water above.

The amount of light puzzled him for a moment until he reasoned that it came from the reflection of the surface light on the grayish sand of the ocean floor. He put his hand on the sand. He knew his hands were very cold, but the water temperature at this depth was not much more than forty degrees. Even so, the sand felt colder. It was soft as silk, and this very softness accentuated its deadness.

He flipped up some of the sand with his fingers. It did not spread out but fell in a lump, all the grains together, back to the ocean floor.

Pressure. The sand was compacted by the weight of water. At this depth there was a pressure on his body of something approaching fifty pounds per square inch. His lungs, accustomed to holding air at a little over fourteen pounds per square inch, were now accommodating air at three or maybe four times that pressure. But his chest and lungs did not explode because of the pressure of the water around him.

He caught a glimpse of his arm. On the surface, clad in the rubber of his wetsuit, it had looked swollen and cumbersome. Now he could make out the formation of the muscles. The pressure had compacted the rubber of the suit to perhaps half its size, revealing the true outline of his arm.

He turned to look for Tom and Shirley. They floated above him, distinctly seen, very graceful, and utterly silent. Though he could see the bubbles escaping from their regulators as they exhaled, there was no sound from them. They were like two black, slow-moving ghosts—dumb creatures, incapable of making any noise, more dead than alive.

The bubbles they emitted were pinpoints which increased in size as they ascended toward the top. He listened carefully for any tiny sound in this mute world. There was none. Even the concertina doors of the trolley, opening and shutting ceaselessly, were utterly quiet.

Suddenly he felt terribly alone. Shirley and Tom had glided over the top of the trolley down to the other side

[93]

and disappeared from view. He looked around. There was nothing to be seen but the gray dead sand disappearing gently into an undefined horizon. The appalling isolation and absence of noise frightened him.

Why had Shirley and Tom disappeared? They were not supposed to do that. He wanted to see them desperately and immediately. Being alone here was like being buried alive in a huge cold tomb. And he was alone—absolutely alone, without sound or sight of any living creature, as if he had been placed on the appalling landscape of the moon. As these black thoughts mounted, he wanted to dart over the trolley car in panic and find his two companions, but he deliberately fought down the rising sense of dread.

I am all right, he told himself. I am able to breathe easily. I am utterly safe. Even saying these things to himself calmed him. He looked away from the trolley out into the infinite gloom of the depths. There was something tremendously serene and beautiful about them. Deserted of all movement and of all sound, they spoke of a great peace —a peace like eternity.

It's beautiful here, he said to himself. I have never seen anything as beautiful as this. Nothing on earth is so lovely. How wonderful it would be just to wander off into that immeasurable depth of the ocean, moving as gracefully and easily as a fish, and forget all those conflicts of the mind and living that plague me on the surface.

But that is not the way I must think, he said to himself. It is beautiful and I will never forget how lovely it is. But I belong to the surface and must not be lured away from the trolley car because there is death out there.

A movement in the green gloom that bounded him at a distance that he could not estimate attracted his attention. Some dark vague shape had come almost into the margin

[94]

of visibility and gone away again. The sight did not frighten him. Then there was another movement from the far end of the trolley car, and Tom and Shirley came into view. The very sight of them made him feel cheerful; he wanted to reach out and touch them.

Shirley glided over to him and held open the swinging door of the trolley. The invitation was plain. With a slight flick of his flippers, he went inside. There was an immediate lessening of light, as if sudden twilight had descended.

He swam gently down the aisle between the seats, which were covered with algae. He touched one of them. It was as slippery as a newly unfleshed bone. He sat down on a seat and Shirley and Tom floated down the aisle toward him and sat down also.

This trolley car never thought to be in such a place or to have three such strangely clad passengers, Chuck said to himself, and smiled at the idea. He noticed that bubbles were collecting on the roof of the trolley car, making a single bubble. It would probably remain there until the roof disintegrated—a silent proof that some living creature had entered the trolley while it was at the bottom of the sea.

They went out through the windows, and Tom signaled them to follow him. The trolley was anchored to the bottom by a cable, which led outward from it into the green gloom of the depths.

They followed this out, swimming side by side. Chuck found that even while swimming he sank gently to the ash gray sand of the bottom. But he could push himself off with one hand. Experimenting, he found that a finger was enough to raise him. He was almost, but not quite, weightless.

Not a single scrap of weed, not a stone or a piece of debris, lay on the surface of the submarine desert over which

[95]

they were gliding. Chuck glanced back and found that the trolley car had disappeared. If he had succumbed to his earlier urge to swim away from the trolley car, he might never have found it again. Though the visibility seemed great, it was hardly more than twenty feet.

Looking ahead, he saw something moving on the bottom, a glistening gray shape. He came up to it and found it was a huge snail. Its shell was as big as his fist, and its soft satiny body spilled out underneath the shell. There was something noble and stately in this enormous snail out on some pilgrimage of its own in the desolation. To where was it bound and how had it found its way?

Tom pointed to two black dots on the bottom and Chuck knew they were the eyes of a crab buried in the sand. There was life here, then. But it was hidden life. The hunter and the hunted still existed in this cold but serene world.

Chuck was swimming only a foot or two above the bottom. Suddenly the bottom exploded before his faceplate, and in a panic he kicked upward. Then he saw a flat shape undulate away from him into the gloom. He had disturbed a large halibut asleep in the sand and buried all but its eyes.

They reached the end of the cable, found that it was fastened to a huge block of concrete, and started back again. Chuck was ahead. He was looking along the line of the cable, waiting for the trolley car to appear. A movement to his left distracted him and then he froze in terror, holding on to the cable.

Out of the obscurity came a lovely torpedo-shaped creature—a shark. Even in his terror he was struck by its elegance, by the sleekness of its lines and the exquisite sickle shapes of its pectoral and dorsal fins and tail. It glided obliquely toward them without the slightest effort.

[96]

The under part was white and the upper part a darker shade. There was one white spot on the upper part of the tail. All this Chuck noticed even as he froze with terror. He could not move, but was riveted to the cable. He could feel his pulse pounding in his ears until he was sure he must go deaf from the sound, and the shark must hear the beating of his heart quite plainly.

He wanted to surface immediately, to get out of the ocean and never come back again. Failing that, he wanted to get behind the others, to put them between him and danger. He did neither of these things because he was incapable of movement. The shark approached majestically until Chuck could see its fierce cruel eye, the slits of its gills, and its mouth, a black sickle-shape under its protruding snout.

And then, quite suddenly, Chuck's fear changed to rage.

Why should he, a superior creature, submit to this remnant of prehistoric times? With anger came the ability to move.

He turned and saw Shirley behind him. She was plainly terrified. Tom had moved from the cable toward Chuck. Then he turned in the water so that his back was to Chuck's and their two lungs bumped against each other with a dull bell-like note.

The effect on the shark was laughable. He was gone in a second. One quiver of his body, and he shot off into the gloom, and the rage that had mounted in Chuck changed to contempt.

Then he remembered the shape he had seen when he was alone by the trolley. Had it been the same shark? Had the shark sighted or scented him and thought him alone? And what could he have done against the creature if he were attacked by himself?

[97]

He instantly felt a great friendship for Tom and for Shirley too. Shirley was still clinging to the cable, looking fearfully around. Chuck put his clenched fist before his faceplate, the thumb up as a signal of victory. Then they went back to the trolley car.

Tom took the lead, Shirley was in the middle, and Chuck brought up the rear. Now and again Chuck glanced behind him, thinking that the shark might come after them again. He was glad when they got back to the trolley. They circled it a couple of times again, Tom pointing to an encrustation of barnacles on the wooden sides. Then Chuck began to feel some difficulty in breathing. He pulled hard on his mouthpiece but did not seem to get sufficient air to fill his lungs.

Am I still frightened he wondered? Is that why I am trying to take big gulps of air? But he did not feel frightened though it was becoming increasingly difficult to breath. Then it struck him that he had exhausted the air in his lung.

He touched Tom to get his attention and banged with his clenched fist on his chest, the underwater signal that his air supply was running short. Tom nodded. Chuck reached behind him and got hold of his reserve supply lever and pulled it down. Immediately it became easy to breathe again. Tom signaled that they should start up to the surface, and they went up together, disregarding the chain.

Chuck remembered to put his head far back and look directly up to the surface. This lined up his windpipe so that the compressed air in his lungs was able to get out readily while ascending. He remembered also not to pass the smallest of his bubbles. This was not difficult deep down but as he got higher in the water, and gained more

[98]

buoyancy, he had to make a distinct effort to slow his rate of ascent.

Suddenly they left the cold dead water of the deeps. A wonderful warmth enveloped him.

The water above, looking toward the surface, took on a beautiful pearly light. It was warm and glorious and teeming with the very soul of life. It filled him with joy, as if he were being born again, resurrected from the grave. He luxuriated in its milky soft warmth. This was the region of the primeval seas in which life had been born and he knew now the truth of this, for he could feel the warmth of the water and the abounding life in it.

When finally he broke the surface into the splendid sunlight and saw the brisk happy movement of the waves, the blue canopy of the sky, and the white clouds, he was so happy that he wanted to shout with sheer exuberance.

He took off his faceplate and shouted to Tom. "Isn't it great?" he asked. "The sunshine, I mean."

Tom didn't reply. He just grinned. "What do you think of sharks now?" he asked.

"Scared the daylights out of me," said Chuck. "Gosh. I just froze on that cable. Couldn't move. Then I got mad. Don't ask me why."

"Off the record, I was scared too," said Tom. "They always give me the horrors."

"About the guy with the whales," said Shirley. "You were right. If I'd had a camera, I couldn't even have pointed it at the shark, let alone worked it. Ugh. I've never seen anything so cruel in all my life. Next time let's take a camera. Maybe we could get some pictures—if there weren't any sharks around."

"You mean you really were scared?" asked Tom. "You who are always so anxious to be doing some diving?"

"Yes," said Shirley, "I was scared. Real scared."

"That's a change," said Tom. "Come on, we can't hang around here all day treading water. Let's go ashore."

"My tank's about out," said Chuck. He was thinking of getting through the surf after first swimming the quarter of a mile to the surf line.

"Swim on your back," said Tom. "If you get really tired, you can take your tank off and tow it. But it'll give you trouble in the surf so it's best to keep it on. Take it easy. And when you get into the surf, don't fight. Just let the surf wash you in. It will put you ashore eventually."

They set out, Chuck swimming on his back, kicking with his feet. Shirley still had some air in her tank, and Tom, who knew how to be economical in his use of air, had plenty. But they stayed together and made their way ashore without any trouble. Indeed the worst part of the whole adventure was standing up and wading ashore when they got to shallow water.

Tom achieved this readily enough. Chuck was so weak that he fell several times before he could maintain his balance and support himself upright. Shirley had to take her lung and weight belt off. Tom carried her weight belt, and Chuck dragged her lung up to a place where they could pick it up later.

It had been a wonderful adventure that Chuck was never to forget.

XII.

AFTER THAT first deep dive, Chuck went down many times in the ocean, sometimes with Tom and Shirley, sometimes alone with Tom, and sometimes alone with Buzzie Harper, the lifeguard who had brought the art of surfing to one area of New Zealand.

That first dive outside the breakwater enormously enlarged his world. He could move around undersea in a strange, beautiful, and at the same time fearful landscape, a landscape which contained at one and the same time a deepened appeal and a deepened menace for him.

There were times when he vowed that he would never dive again, telling himself that the risks involved were too great to take. Yet when the opportunity to dive came, he always went, putting aside his fears, assuring himself that all would be well and that he was as safe at twenty fathoms as he was on land.

He even hunted around for paying jobs after school with which to finance his diving, for each time he went down he had to rent a suit and lung and regulator, which cost eight dollars. Going down four times a month meant that he had to find thirty-two dollars of his own money to cover equipment rental.

His father, finding Chuck for the first time interested in getting a job after school, was delighted. "That boy is going to amount to something after all," he said to his wife. "He got some good out of that talk I gave him a little while back."

He did not know that Chuck still regarded him as a failure, a man who had missed the main work of living, contenting himself with the ownership of a paint store in a small California city. "That is not the life for me," Chuck often assured himself.

When he thought that he might end up as the proprietor of the same little paint store, he became depressed and listless and lost all ambition. Life on those terms was not worth living. Diving was his only antidote for such a mood —plunging out of the world into the liveliness, the strangeness, the silence, and the menace of the ocean bottom. Indeed, he found in the ocean the only solace for all the things that troubled him—the difficulty of coming to terms with himself and with the world.

"He is maladjusted," the family doctor once told Mrs. Crawford when she discussed with him Chuck's sudden changes from cheerfulness to depression and listlessness.

"He is a teen-ager," Chuck's mother replied. "He lives in a nether-world that you and I have forgotten about because we grew out of it. Or maybe as teen-agers we didn't suffer as badly as Chuck does."

"Well, he'd better grow out of it," said the doctor.

"Some people don't, you know. They remain teen-agers for the rest of their lives, unable to get into any proper proportion with the rest of the world."

Of all the people he knew, Chuck felt that Tom alone really understood his confusions of mind and emotion, and as a result of this and also because they dived together frequently, Chuck grew closer and closer to the stocky lifeguard. He sensed something in common between himself and Tom; something that did not have to be expressed. Sometimes he thought this bond was the ocean, which they both loved and in which they both found a kind of solace. And yet there was not a single occasion when he went diving that Chuck did not experience a sense of dread.

Once he decided to confess this to Tom, feeling that Tom would perhaps supply an explanation that would banish his dread. But Tom didn't do so.

"If you didn't feel that way about diving," said Tom, "I'd try and stop you ever going down again. Sometimes I wonder whether Shirley should be diving at all. She's far too much of the daredevil. At least she seems to be. When you go into the ocean you are not safe unless you take all your equipment and a sense of caution as well. Confidence you get by reflecting that your equipment is in good shape, and checking that it is before each dive. But overconfidence gets more people into trouble on the bottom than any other factor—except panic. Even when you've checked your equipment, you have to realize you are going into a place you are not designed by nature to enter. The ocean will not tolerate arrogance."

"I may not be able to go diving for a while," said Chuck. "Eight dollars every time for equipment just about clears me out."

[103]

"Why don't you buy your own gear?" asked Tom.

"Costs too much," said Chuck. "I've been figuring it up and it costs around three hundred dollars. I haven't got that kind of money."

"You could make it," replied Tom.

"Not on the odd jobs I can get, and do my homework as well," replied Chuck.

Tom made no reply to this immediately. When he did, what he said seemed beside the point.

"I liked the way you reacted when we saw that white shark down by the trolley car," he said.

"I was scared stiff—and I mean stiff," said Chuck. "I couldn't move. If that shark had come in to attack, he could have bitten my leg off and I couldn't have got out of the way."

"You were scared stiff at first. Then you snapped out of it," said Tom. "And when you snapped out of it you didn't panic and head for the top, dropping your weight belt, and leaving me and Shirley to face the music. That's what I mean about liking the way you reacted."

"What's this got to do with the price of diving equipment?" asked Chuck.

"Got a lot to do with it," replied Tom. "You remember that airplane that went down off of Palos Verdes?"

"Yes."

"Buzzie and I were down looking at it the other day. The engines are in good shape. So are the props."

"So?" said Chuck.

"On the bottom they are worth nothing. On top they're worth about four or five thousand dollars as salvage. A salvage company has bought the wreck and asked Buzzie and me to go down and get some lines around the fore part of the plane so they can bring it up. They'll pay two thou-

[104]

sand dollars. We'll need a third diver to stand by down there and lend a hand. Buzzie and I will be pretty busy handling the lines.

"It's kind of dangerous working around all that jagged metal and it's easy to get fouled on a line under water. If a line pinches an air hose, a diver can lose consciousness fast, even before his buddy knows about it. So we need a third man, a safety man. I talked to Buzzie and he agreed you might be the person to approach. We'd split the fee equally. You'd get something over six hundred dollars. What do you say?"

"Right now I don't know what to say," said Chuck. "I'll have to think it over."

"Here're a few factors to consider," said Tom. "The plane is down in twenty fathoms—a hundred and twenty feet. We can stay down at that depth for eighteen minutes and not have to decompress. If we stay down any longer —and we may have to—we'll have to stop on the way up and decompress. You'd have to face the prospect of holding on to a line twenty or thirty feet under the surface and staying there for half an hour or so. Maybe alone. That can be trying on your nerves.

"We'll use twin lungs to double our air supply, but even so, one of us, if he has to decompress for a long time and has used up too much air, may run out and have to change lungs under water. You've gone through that training already in the pool, but it's a different deal when it's done in the ocean.

"However, I think you are now competent to handle yourself on a salvage job. And here's a chance to make some money and get some new experience at the same time. But think it over. If you decide you want in, you'd better clear with your parents. I'll talk to them if you wish

[105]

and give them the picture. If they say no—that's it. But I think they'll say yes."

"Well, I'll think about it," repeated Chuck. "When do you have to know?"

"In a couple of days," said Tom. "Meanwhile Buzzie and I will map out the whole strategy and get a good fix on the plane. It's buoyed, the tail section, that is. We have to get the fore part properly buoyed and wait for good weather as well. There's no rush."

"Will you use a barge on the surface to pull the thing up when you have the lines around it?" asked Chuck.

"That was our first idea," said Tom. "But barges with derricks come high and will cut into the profit. Probably what we'll do is tie some fifty gallon drums on the wings with cables and then pump air into them from the surface. The air will lift the whole thing up. Of course the drums will explode when they get to the top. But we'll have a cradle around the plane to haul in on from a surface barge so that the wreck won't sink again when the drums explode."

When he got home, Chuck had plenty to think about. The prospect of earning something over six hundred dollars for what would be less than a day's work appealed strongly. He'd been down in twenty fathoms before and had no trouble. But there had been no wreckage around, no sharp pieces of twisted metal, no gasoline and oil seeping from engines, and no lines to get fouled in or drums filled with air to come roaring up through the water if they broke their moorings.

Why, he wondered, had Tom approached him about the job? There were plenty of others among the lifeguards who would have been glad of the chance. Was it because of friendship, or because he really believed that Chuck was

[106]

especially qualified to help? Or was he trying to get him, Chuck, to prove something about himself?

This kind of speculation, Chuck decided, was senseless. The problem was a simple one. Did he want to earn six hundred dollars on a diving job or not? That was all there was to it. Would he risk his life for six hundred dollars?

Vaguely he sensed that he had been issued a subtle challenge by Tom. Life these days seemed to consist of them. There was the original one about going on with his diving lessons when he had been scared by the shark attack on Tom and Buzzie. There was the challenge of going down inside the harbor. And then of going down in open water to the trolley car. And now here was this challenge to work on the salvage of the plane. Why didn't people stop challenging him, he asked himself. Why didn't they just leave him alone instead of confronting him again and again with a challenge, each more difficult than the last? He didn't want them. He just wanted to be left by himself to develop in his own way.

All right. He wouldn't accept. He would tell Tom that he had thought the matter over and decided he didn't want to help with the salvage of the plane.

For a few moments the decision comforted him. And then he wondered what Shirley would say when she heard. He tried to tell himself that what she said didn't matter. But it did. He found to his surprise that he was anxious to win her approval. And he was anxious also to have the continuing approval of Tom.

"I'll talk to Dad about it," he said. "Maybe he'll forbid it. And that will settle the question and nobody can blame me then if I don't take the job."

XIII.

WHEN MR. CRAWFORD came home from work each day, the first thing he did was take a shower and change his clothes. He did this, he said, to get rid of the smell of the paint in the store. Then he had a glass of beer while sitting on the patio at the back of the house to read his paper.

He read the notices of new construction in the town first, then the sports news, and then the international news. The newspaper he subscribed to was of a conservative character and did not make much display of crime news. Mr. Crawford held that stories of robberies and beatings and murders were proper fare for the police but not for a decent home. Chuck thought that his father was unrealistic in this attitude, closing his eyes to anything in the world around him that hinted at the violence of his fellows.

"I saw enough violence in World War II," said Mr. Crawford once. "A man's home is his castle. He should let into it only the things that are healthful for his home. Murder isn't."

It was an unwritten rule of the Crawford house that until this ritual of his father's had been performed, no one started a conversation with him. When he was ready for talk, Mr. Crawford signaled his readiness by putting the paper by his chair and saying aloud to nobody in particular, "That Castro will come to no good end," or, "If the Dodgers don't find themselves a pitcher, they might as well take up softball," or, "The only boxer who was worth going half a block to see was Joe Louis." Having made a pronouncement on whatever item of the news affected him, Mr. Crawford was ready for general conversation.

Chuck had to sweat out this ritual, then, before he could broach the subject of the salvage job to his father. When the time for talk had finally come on this particular day, he said, "Dad, you know that I've been doing a lot of scuba diving recently."

"Hum," said Mr. Crawford. This was an expression he used to signify that he had heard what was said but did not necessarily agree with the statement.

"Well, I've got a chance to make six hundred dollars diving now, but I want your advice. It's kind of dangerous."

"What's it all about?" he asked.

Chuck told him. He described the offer, outlined as best he could the hazards involved. This was difficult because Mr. Crawford knew little or nothing of scuba diving, and Chuck had found that those who knew nothing of the subject, thought the whole activity suicidal. He also explained why Tom had approached him on the matter—because he had not panicked when they saw the shark near the trolley car.

"But why I didn't panic I don't know," said Chuck honestly. "And I'm not sure that if I saw another shark down there, I still wouldn't panic."

"Mother," shouted Mr. Crawford when Chuck had done. "Do you know that your son frightened off a shark the other day?" And then he said something that for him was very rare. "Now there's something that I never did when I was a boy." He was beaming with pride.

In that moment Chuck sensed a change in the relationship that existed between himself and his father. His father no longer regarded him as a junior, inferior, and somewhat useless member of the family. He was accepting Chuck on something of his own level, allowing Chuck into his own world. It was the first time Chuck could recall his father having admired anything he had done. But he was immediately fearful that his father would make too much of it, and brag about the episode at Kiwanis next time he went to a meeting.

"Look, Dad," he said, "it was just a matter of luck that I didn't panic and that the shark was frightened off. Our tanks hit under water, made a noise, and the shark took off like a rabbit. That's all there was to it."

"Not luck at all," said his father. "Panicking means losing your self-control. Holding on to your self-control isn't luck. It's a deliberate act you have to force yourself to do.

"When I was your age I was up on a scaffold painting some windows on the fifteenth floor. There was a high wind and the scaffold was swaying. Suddenly my end of

[110]

it started to go. The knot I had made around the ropes worked loose because of the swaying of the scaffold, and the ropes started running through the pulleys. For a moment, like you, I was frozen stiff with fright. Then I grabbed the ropes—all of them—and held them in my hands. The scaffold steadied and the painter who was with me tied the ropes fast again. When we got down, the painter gave me a painter's hat. He wouldn't let me wear one before because I was only an apprentice.

"'You're still not a very good painter,' he said, 'but you're entitled to wear a painter's hat.' That was a great day in my life."

"Well," said Chuck, "I'm scared of going down on that salvage job." The words came out of him because he was, in this new relationship with his father, anxious to be completely honest with him. He wanted to be through with the pretenses of ability and courage he had found himself employing, almost without being aware of them, in the past. "I was kind of hoping," he continued, "that you would forbid me to go."

"Well, I'm not going to forbid you," said his father. "Not now anyway. Not until I've had a talk with Tom and found out whether you really know what you're doing when you're diving."

"Tom says I've got enough experience," said Chuck.

"Maybe. I still want to know why he picked you instead of one of the other lifeguards," replied his father, and that closed the discussion for the time being.

That evening Shirley called Chuck. "It's a lovely night," she said. "The tide's low and I've been down to the beach and there isn't any surf at all."

"So?" said Chuck.

[111]

"So I thought maybe we could go diving together. I would like to find out what it's like at night and I've got all the equipment."

"Not me," said Chuck. "I've got some work to do."

"I'm sorry you can't make it," said Shirley. "I'm going anyway."

"Where's Tom?" asked Chuck.

"He's down in San Diego and won't be back for a day," was the reply.

"You know you're not to go diving by yourself," said Chuck sternly. "That's suicide. That's the first rule."

"I'm only going inside the harbor," said Shirley. "And besides, someone is coming with me."

"Who?"

"Fred Manners."

The name was familiar. Chuck remembered that Fred Manners was a scuba diver he had met up at the Dive 'N Surf. They had discussed diving together, but nothing had come of it except an exchange of telephone numbers.

"O.K. So long as someone is going with you. Sorry I can't make it."

"I'm sorry, too," said Shirley. Her voice sounded slightly hostile, and she hung up without any farewells.

An hour later Chuck was busy with some problems involving logarithms, but he could not put his mind on his work. He kept thinking of Shirley going diving at night in the harbor. They'd been down at night a couple of times together with Tom, but that wasn't really enough experience for Shirley to branch out on her own with an unknown diver. Then, on a hunch, he decided to call Fred Manners. Fred answered the phone himself.

"I thought you had gone diving with Shirley," said Chuck.

[112]

"Nope," said Fred. "She called me and asked me to go but I couldn't."

"Hope she didn't go by herself," said Chuck, his heart sinking.

"She isn't that crazy," said Fred.

Chuck next dialed Shirley's number, but there was no reply. That could mean that she had gone out. It could also mean that she was diving alone. What was the smart thing to do? He could drive around to Shirley's house, but since she didn't answer the phone, he would learn nothing. He called Buzzie at the lifeguard station and explained the situation to him.

"You don't know where she was thinking of diving in the harbor, do you?" asked Buzzie. "That's a pretty big area."

"No," said Chuck. "But you know that place where the bulldozers were working and they're putting out a new mole? The place where that small bulldozer toppled over and went into the water? Well, she talked to me about going over and taking a look at the bulldozer down there before they pull it up."

"That's a good enough lead," said Buzzie. "Come on over and I'll get some gear for you. We'll take a look down there. Nobody at the station knows about any lone scuba diver going down in the harbor tonight. But it's possible she went in without our knowing it."

Chuck was soon at the lifeguard station, and Buzzie threw him a wetsuit. "Get into that," he said. "I'll go down with you and we'll make a search. The water's clear anyway. Wonder where she would get diving gear from anyway?"

"Probably borrowed Tom's—if she went down," said Chuck.

[113]

"She'd look a little silly in Tom's wetsuit," said Buzzie. "Tom's got a wetsuit that would fit a short whale."

"Maybe she didn't use it," said Chuck. "The water's not so cold once you get used to it. And she wouldn't be going deep in the harbor."

They had soon put on their wetsuits and drove with the rest of their gear to the mole where they thought Shirley might be diving. Chuck began to feel that perhaps he was making too much of the incident. All he knew for sure was that Shirley had wanted to go diving, had not had the partner she expected, and wasn't at home. She might simply have gone out in a huff.

When they got to the place where the bulldozer had toppled into the water, they put on their tanks and weight belts and surveyed the surface of the water. It was a dull gray under the stars, merging into blackness farther out.

"Can't see a thing from up here," said Buzzie. "Come on. Stay close." He put his mouthpiece in place, switched on his waterproof flashlight, and waded in with Chuck beside him.

The bottom shelved steeply downward. Four feet from the partially constructed mole they were up to their chests. It was, however, both clear and calm. Chuck prepared his faceplate against fogging, put it on, and ducked down behind Buzzie. His flashlight showed a golden path through the water, a path that disappeared into nothing. He was on the bottom before he was ready, bumping into the sand and dislodging his faceplate, which filled with water. He cleared it and glided alongside Buzzie, their two flashlights illuminating the bottom ahead. There was, once again, the always surprising silence of the underseas, a silence that was inviting and at the same time menacing.

[114]

A little perch appeared suddenly in the beam of the flashlights, shining an entrancing silver and brighter than any star. It rendered itself invisible in a moment by the simple process of turning head on to the beams.

They came to an area where a current stirred up the sand. It seemed to Chuck they were approaching a sandhill on the bottom and he started to go up. Then he found that the sandhill was only millions of particles of sand, glittering in his light.

For a moment he lost Buzzie, but diving down through the solid-seeming hill, which was nothing but a lot of sand under water, found him below. He looked about, over to his left, for a gleam in the water that might come from Shirley's flashlight. He saw nothing.

Buzzie edged to the right, and they came on the bulldozer. There were lines attached to the towbar by which it could be hauled out the next day. They circled the bulldozer but found no trace of Shirley, and Chuck was almost convinced that he had brought Buzzie out on a wild-goose chase. The front of the bulldozer was buried in the bottom sand. It seemed that after the bulldozer fell into the water, there had been a submarine landslide which had buried the nose.

They inspected this area but saw no sign of Shirley. Then, just as they were about to turn away, Chuck saw one bubble come up from under the sand. He reached to Buzzie, tapping him on the leg, and pointed. At the same moment, another bubble came up through the sand over the front of the bulldozer. It could be just a pocket of air trapped beneath the sand which was gradually coming up. But it also could be Shirley.

The two started digging, scooping the sand aside with their hands. It was Chuck who came on her first. He found

[115]

her swim fin sticking up through the sand, still on her foot.

He uncovered a leg and felt it, but it was cold and he could not tell whether she was alive. Buzzie uncovered an arm, which was limp, and digging furiously with Chuck's help, got Shirley's head and shoulders free. She had been buried by a landslide while swimming around the bulldozer and was unconscious, though her mouthpiece was still in place, her teeth clamped hard on it. But she was not breathing. The dirt had fouled her regulator, and she was getting no air.

The few bubbles that had come up through the sand and brought about her rescue were leaking out of one of the ruptured tubes. The two of them dragged Shirley free, came to the surface, and pulled her ashore. There Buzzie applied artificial respiration using the mouth to mouth method. After a little while, Shirley showed signs of life.

Chuck returned to the pickup they had used to drive down to the mole. He was in such a hurry that he forgot to take off his tanks and couldn't get into the cab. He struggled out of the tank harness, took off his fins, and drove over to the lifeguard station to get an ambulance.

Never dive alone, he kept saying to himself. Never dive alone. For the first time, he was really aware of just how vital that rule was.

XIV.

THE UNDER-WATER ACCIDENT to Shirley, which nearly cost her life, kept her in a hospital for two days and completely broke her nerve. She would have nothing to do with scuba diving and did not even like to hear the subject mentioned. She had been through an experience very close to being buried alive as a result of her own folly. She knew it would not have occurred if she had obeyed the basic rule of always diving with a buddy. Nonetheless, the shock was so great that she could not bring herself to dive again. There was no need for Tom to upbraid her for diving alone. She had had a far crueler punishment than any he could mete out, and for many nights afterward she lived her experience over and over again in dreams.

She was indeed lucky to be alive. Had Chuck and Buzzie been a few minutes later in finding her, had Chuck not suggested the particular area of the harbor in which to search for her first, she might never have been revived. She had, as Tom said privately to Chuck, become arrogant, and the ocean never forgives arrogance.

As for Chuck, he was deeply shaken by this near-tragedy in only ten feet of water. All his anxieties over undertaking the salvage job with Tom and Buzzie returned afresh. And yet he found a kind of stubbornness in himself that prevented his going directly to Tom and saying that he was too scared to go ahead with the project.

"I haven't even got the guts to confess that I'm scared and want out," he told himself miserably time and time again. Tom meanwhile had a talk with Mr. Crawford about the job.

"Is Chuck really competent as a diver?" Mr. Crawford asked.

"Yes," said Tom, "completely competent. More than that, he has a natural affinity for the water. He has an understanding of it that lots of divers never learn. I've seen experienced divers get really frightened when they're caught by wave motion and rammed up against rocks. They try to fight off and cut themselves up and lose their heads generally. Chuck doesn't. He just waits until the wave has passed and then comes off the rocks with the aftersuck. Little things like that you can't teach some people. But Chuck comes by them naturally. Buzzie and I are both agreed that he is a natural diver, like there are some people who are natural racing drivers and others who are natural horsemen. He knows the sea. He works with it instead of against it."

"Fine," said Mr. Crawford. "Now just why did you ask Chuck to help with this job? I'm sure there are other divers available with more experience than he. Was it to give him an opportunity of earning something like six hundred dollars?"

"That was part of it," said Tom. "There's a good and exciting career ahead for competent scuba divers who really have some talent for the work. I don't mean just commercial diving for abalone and lobsters. That's the diving equivalent of working on a farm as a hired hand.

"I mean as a marine biologist or a marine archaeologist. Marine biology is, in a sense, in its infancy. Studies of marine life have been made almost entirely on land with creatures taken out of the sea in nets. But now there is a whole field of research for scientists who can go under water and study marine life in its natural surroundings. And as for marine archaeology, there are vast treasures relating to man's past lying on the bottom of the ocean waiting to be found and studied, not by amateurs, but by trained archaeologists. Here are two big careers in new fields ahead of Chuck if he wants to follow them.

"So the six hundred dollars is a kind of a bait. It will help him buy his equipment and have a little left over toward his college expenses when he leaves high school at the end of the year.

"But there's more to it than that. Chuck's having a hard time growing up. He's all mixed up, as you and I know, confused about his future and his worth and so on. I expect he's talked to you about that at times."

Mr. Crawford sighed. "To be frank," he said, "he hasn't. There are times when I don't understand the boy at all and think he just isn't aggressive and is afraid of competition. When I was a boy—"

"When you were a boy you lived in a pretty uncomplicated world," Tom cut in. "Anyway you weren't Chuck. You were a different kind of boy. Chuck's a sensitive guy

[119]

and anybody who's sensitive is full of self-doubts and takes little failures seriously. All that Chuck needs to grow up is self-confidence and with it the feeling that he can measure up to a responsibility."

"Right," said Mr. Crawford. "When I was a boy anything I had to do I did. People could rely on me."

"You mind if I give you a piece of advice?" Tom asked.

"No," said Mr. Crawford, "never turned down a free offer of advice in my life."

"O.K.," said Tom. "Stop saying 'When I was a boy' to Chuck all the time. Just the words themselves imply that he is your inferior. That doesn't help his self-confidence at all.

"And about responsibility. That's what I'm leading up to. On this salvage job Chuck will have plenty of responsibility in an area in which he is competent: diving. He'll be responsible for his own safety and for my safety and for Buzzie's—as we will be responsible for him. That's a pretty big order for a sixteen-year-old boy, and if he handles it, he'll grow bigger and stronger inside and be on his way to being a man. And being a man is the object of being a boy. That's what Chuck is going to get out of the ocean—manhood, though he doesn't know it yet. That's why I want him to come with us on this salvage dive."

"What if he decides he doesn't want to do it?"

"He'll do it," said Tom. Then he grinned. "When I was a boy," he said, "I did. I took on things I was halfway scared of. And so did you. And so will Chuck. Only don't pressure him. Just leave him alone. Let him make his own decision. That's the biggest part of what he's going to learn."

"Will you think less of him if he decides against the project?" asked Mr. Crawford, somewhat anxiously.

[120]

"No," said Tom, "I won't." Then he added, "What I mean is, I'll try not to."

Two days later Chuck went round to Tom's house, ostensibly to see how Shirley was. They were alone for a while, sitting at the edge of Tom's pool, and after some small talk Shirley said suddenly, "Chuck, you're not going down on that airplane salvage job, are you?"

"Haven't made up my mind," said Chuck.

"Don't go," said Shirley very earnestly. "Please don't go. I'm frightened that something will happen to you. I'm sure that something will."

Chuck gave her a quick look. She was so different from the old Shirley, always anxious to do something new in diving, that it shocked him to realize how much she had changed. Her fear was likely to last throughout her life unless something was done to remove it.

"I've just made up my mind," he said. "I'm going to take that salvage job."

"Why?" demanded Shirley.

"I didn't have a good reason before," said Chuck. "Six hundred dollars didn't seem enough of a reason, though I need the money. And Tom's story about needing another man didn't quite ring true. But now I have a good reason: you."

"I forbid you to do it because of me," flared Shirley. "I won't have anything to do with it. What a horrible thing to say! If anything happened to you, I'd have it on my conscience all my life."

"Nothing will happen to me," said Chuck calmly. "And if I left you as scared as you are for the rest of your days, I'd have *that* on *my* conscience all my life."

Instead of replying, Shirley got up and went to her room and slammed the door. When Tom came in (he had

[121]

been shopping with his wife) Chuck said simply, "I'm going to take that diving job if it's still open."

"Give me two bucks, honey," said Tom to his wife. "You just lost a bet." Turning to Chuck he added, grinning, "Women don't understand men at all. She figured you'd want out. Where's Shirley?"

Chuck explained, and Mary went to Shirley's room, knocked on the door, and entered. After a few minutes they both returned. It was plain that Shirley had been crying.

"We both think you are idiots," said Mary, "and you can give me back those two dollars, Tom Prior. The two of you are going to be sitting around here all evening talking about your silly diving, and Shirley and I are going to a movie."

"You can go if you want to," said Tom, "but I'd sooner you stayed."

"Why?" demanded Mary.

"I'm going to call Buzzie to come over for a conference, and I'd like Shirley in on it," said Tom. "She's got a pretty good head, and she might help us with a couple of details."

"Such as?" demanded Mary.

"Oh, all right," said Tom, who began to see that his stratagem to get Shirley at least to listen to some diving talk was clumsy.

"We'll stay," said Mary in a small voice. "It's the least we can do."

Chuck stayed at Tom's house for dinner, and Buzzie came over afterward. They gathered in the living room with cups of coffee to discuss their plans.

"I've been talking to the design department of the people who made the plane," said Buzzie. "They tell me that

[122]

the forward section, with engines intact and undercarriage, weighs around five thousand pounds. That's dead weight on land and doesn't really mean much.

"It means something when the plane is brought to the surface, because we must have a barge with a crane capable of supporting two and a half tons. But to raise the thing, the figure we want is dead weight under water, which has something to do with the amount of water the thing displaces. Anyway, they've come up with a figure for that. After a lot of hemming and hawing, they reckon about two tons."

"Less?" said Chuck surprised.

"Yep. That's the amount of water the thing displaces. On the top you figure dead weight, and on the bottom, water displacement. By the way, if we use air-filled drums to raise the plane, she'll start off pretty slowly from the bottom and accelerate all the way to the top. Might keep on going and become airborne."

"If it comes up under the barge, we'll have the plane on the top and the barge on the bottom in short order," said Tom. Everybody laughed. "Nothing to laugh at," said Tom. "We'll have to figure a way of guiding it so that it comes up alongside the barge and not underneath."

"Just how do we go about this whole thing anyway?" asked Chuck. "I'm not at all clear about it."

"Well, here's the outline," said Tom. "We were thinking of taking cables down, securing them to the plane, and just hauling the thing up by a crane. But that's expensive and the wing section might break up under the stress. So we'll take down a number of fifty-gallon drums, fasten them with cables to the wings, and fill them with air down there. They'll raise the wreck to the surface.

"We'll have to use two barges, one on either side of the

[123]

wreck and some distance off. Each will have a crane, and we'll have to hook the crane cable to the plane. The operators will reel in on the crane cables as the plane comes up. Those drums will explode when they hit the surface or get near to the surface. The cranes will prevent the plane from falling back to the bottom when raised.''

''Won't the two barges be pulled together by the weight of the plane between them?'' asked Chuck.

''They'll be anchored so that won't happen,'' said Tom. ''We'll have a pontoon of empty drum barrels on the top to hitch the plane to, and float it alongside the harbor where it can be hauled ashore. Then we collect our check.''

''How do we fill those drums under water?'' asked Buzzie. ''That's what's bothering me. We have to fill them with water to take them down. Then we have to lash them to the plane and fill them with air down there.''

''We'll have to have an air pump on one of the salvage barges and take an airline down to fill the drums,'' said Tom.

''Why not take down lungs and fill the drums with them?'' asked Shirley.

''Huh?'' said Tom, turning to her.

''There're over two thousand pounds of compressed air in a lung,'' said Shirley. ''It costs only a dollar to fill each lung. So it would be cheaper to take a lot of filled lungs down to the bottom and use the air in them to fill the drums. It would be safer too, because you'd have plenty of lungs available if—if anybody needed one.''

''Best idea we've had this evening,'' said Tom. ''I knew you should stay here instead of going to that movie.'' The discussion of plans went on, with Shirley taking a more active part in them.

[124]

XV.

TWO WEEKS LATER, Chuck, Buzzie, and Tom were prepared to make the salvage dive. Twenty fifty-gallon drums had been found and pressure-tested to a hundred pounds per square inch, which was many times the pressure they would have to contain at a hundred and twenty feet below the water. The barges were ready and had taken up station the night before over the wreckage, while the wrecked fore part of the plane had been pinpointed and buoyed so that there would be no delay in finding it on the bottom.

These preparations occupied some part of the two weeks that had elapsed since the first conference on the problem at Tom's house. There were other things that had to be done, too. Two dozen spare lungs had been found, filled, and put on the barges. They would provide an ample supply both for filling the drums with air on the bottom and for the three divers.

Chuck, Tom, and Buzzie had made three practice dives down to the wreckage and Chuck had been given the task of fastening and unfastening a cable clip on a cable under water. He practiced first on land, then on land with his eyes shut, and then under the water. At first he found the task extraordinarily difficult on the bottom. It took him ten times as long, because of the slowing down of his mental processes. But with practice he was able to fasten and unfasten the cable clips without thinking of what he was doing. Then he could do the job with ease at twenty fathoms.

The three of them worked out a drill for handling the drums on the bottom. The drums would be sent down from the barges in advance with a length of cable and a cable clip. The lungs with which they were to be filled with air would be kept on the bottom, going down first. Tom and Buzzie would manhandle each drum into position on the wing of the wrecked plane.

Chuck would wrap the cable around it and the wing, attaching it firmly to the wing, and tighten the cable clip. Then he would stand by until Tom and Buzzie brought him another drum. This was somewhat different from the first proposal that he would be merely a safety man, circling around near the other two, ready to help them if they got into trouble.

"We'll all keep an eye on each other," said Tom. "One eye for the work and one eye for the other divers. The work will go faster, and I think we will be safer that way."

The plan was to attach twenty drums to the wings and then start filling them with air. The drums would be attached so the bungs would be facing down. A hose from a

[126]

lung would be inserted in the bunghole and the lung valve cracked open gently. A jet of air would flow into the drum, driving the water out, and when air bubbles started to come out of the bunghole that would be the signal the drum was full. Buzzie proposed that as each drum was filled, the bung be screwed back in. But Shirley suggested what seemed to be a better idea.

"Why not leave the bung out?" she said. "If the bung is in, the drum will contain about fifty pounds of air per square inch. So it will explode when it gets to the top because the water pressure will be less than fifty pounds per square inch—"

"It shouldn't explode," said Tom, interrupting her. "Those drums are tested to a hundred pounds per square inch. They should hold."

Shirley shook her head. "They're not built to take pressure," she said. "They might get damaged on the bottom a bit and weakened. It isn't necessary to subject them to that amount of pressure. If the bung is left out, then the air in the drum will escape as the surrounding pressure of the water decreases on the way up. It is like breathing out while surfacing. The drums will still be full of air when they get to the top, but the air will be at a pressure of about fourteen pounds per square inch instead of fifty and there should be no danger at all of explosion. In fact, you won't even need a cable from the two barges attached to the wreckage because when it comes to the top the drums will float it there."

"Shirley," said Tom gravely, "you have a natural talent for salvage work." The idea was adopted. It made one barge sufficient for the job, but Tom had a cautious streak in his character and didn't cancel the other barge. He wanted a cable from the two of them attached to the wreckage just in case anything went wrong and the plane started to sink.

Shirley went to the barge with them. She was of two minds whether to go or not, and it took a great effort of will to do so. She went because she realized that it would be more difficult to sit at home waiting for news of how the operation was going. Mary did not go out to the barge. There was an unspoken understanding between herself and Tom that when he was diving she would stay at home. He preferred it that way.

The three divers entered the water at ten minutes past six and were on the bottom two minutes later, taking their time adjusting to the pressure and seeing that their gear, checked out above, was working well. Chuck found that his weight belt was up a little too high on his hips. He was wearing double tanks and was top heavy. He worked it down until he was slightly heavier below the middle. That would be the proper balance for the job ahead. Chuck and Tom had put a few extra pounds of weight on their legs. They would have to do a fair amount of standing on the bottom and this would help keep them upright.

On the bottom Chuck again had the impression of being in a huge air-filled room. Visibility was good. They could see fifty feet with ease. Indeed, the water was so clear that shafts of sunlight played over the bottom reefs like light coming through a window high up in the roof of a gloomy cathedral. Where these beams of light fell—and they moved swiftly back and forth over the bottom because of the wave action on the surface—they lit up an enchanting scene of lovely growths of seaweed and algae.

The rocks of the reef were a royal purple flecked with white and dots of red. Some of the seaweed was dark brown, some pale brown, and some light green. The algae was a light gold. And there was, of course, the incredible silence of the underwater world, a silence both of big things and small things such as is never experienced on land. The slow surge of the ocean was silent and the tiny movements of the strands of algae were silent also. All Chuck could hear were his own bubbles and the noise of his inhalation. He had soon adjusted to these sounds, and they made no impression on him.

The need, as soon as they were on the bottom, was for speed. Twenty feet above the plane Tom had spotted the sunken drums. They were lying all over the bottom among the reefs. He signaled to Buzzie and the two glided over to one, upended it, and with Chuck standing guard on them, brought it over the plane. They put it below the starboard wing, near the fuselage.

Chuck found the length of cable attached to it. He took one end and Tom the other, and they passed it around the drum and over the top of the wing. The cable was too short by about a foot. There was not enough of an overlap to fasten a couple of clips on it.

Chuck was immediately bewildered. He did not know what to do but just looked at the end of the cable in his hand trying to figure out why it was too short.

Tom, however, went into action. A crowbar had been sent down on a line and was near the plane. Tom took it, motioned to the others to stand back, and started knocking a hole in the wing of the plane. The thin metal was easily pierced on both sides. Then he passed the cable through, and signaling to Buzzie, went off to get another drum. They were back with it before Chuck had fastened the cable clip. The wrench, which had fitted the nuts of the cable clip perfectly on the surface, now seemed too small. He could not get it on the nut.

[129]

"Why did it fit up there and it won't fit down here?" Chuck kept asking himself. "It must be something to do with the temperature. It must have shrunk." His mind pondered this problem while he wrestled to get the wrench on the nut. Tom saw his difficulty, took the wrench from him, and reversed it. There were two ends and Chuck had been trying to use the smaller end. On the surface he would have immediately known his mistake. In twenty fathoms, someone had to point it out to him.

"I've got to start using my head," thought Chuck. "Otherwise I'm going to be more of a nuisance than a help down here."

He got the cable clip fastened and then checked the drum over. The bung was on the side instead of the bottom. So he had to loosen the clip again, by which time there were three drums waiting for him. He began to feel annoyed with Tom and Buzzie. They were deliberately stacking up the drums to belittle him. Then he chuckled. What a goofy thought that was. They were doing their work well, but he was fumbling his. That was all there was to it. He'd have to do better.

Buzzie and Tom helped position a couple of drums for Chuck until he had the cable around them and could tighten the nuts. He had soon caught up with them and then there came a period when he had to wait until a drum was brought to him. He had been busy tightening the last cable clip and was not sure in which direction Tom and Buzzie had gone off looking for the drums, which were scattered around on the bottom.

He looked around at the bluish-green envelope that surrounded him. There was no sign of either of them. Well, all that meant, he assured himself, was that they had had to go more than fifty feet away for the drum and so were

[130]

out of sight. He waited a minute but there was no sign of the other two. He searched about for bubbles in the blue obscurity, so clear close to him, so vague a little distance off. There were none. They had no right to go off like this and leave me, he said. They are supposed to keep me in sight at all times. It is as bad as diving alone to be left like this. Then the reverse of what he was thinking occurred to him. He had no right to let his two buddies out of his sight.

He was supposed to keep in visual touch with them. The responsibility was mutual. What should he do? Suppose one of them was in trouble? Suppose they had inadvertently lost sight of the plane and could not find their way back to it? As he thought of these possibilities, Chuck could feel his heart beating faster.

"Slow down," he told himself. "Calm down. Let's think a little. I can't see them so they are more than fifty feet away. That means they can't see the wreckage. O.K. If I circle the plane, keeping it in sight, I can extend my vision by another forty feet or so. That will give me a better chance of finding them. Maybe I should take a spare lung with me. No. If someone's in trouble we can buddy-breathe. If I take a lung, it will slow me down."

He set out from the plane, making an ever-increasing circle around it as he peered into the bluish nothingness constituting his horizon. He was looking for bubbles which would betray the presence of his buddies. Once he saw a silver stream coming from the ocean but it turned out to be a school of perch.

Then, when he was making a circle thirty feet from the plane, he spotted bubble bursts a little distance off and went toward them. He found Tom and Buzzie at the bottom of a beautiful submarine valley.

Tom was leading Buzzie by the hand and one glance told Chuck what was the matter. Buzzie's faceplate had broken. He was almost as blind as a bat. He couldn't clear it because it wouldn't hold air. Tom signaled that he was going to surface with Buzzie. Chuck nodded and decided he was going to surface, too. He didn't want to stay down there alone on the bottom. There was nothing he could do alone, and the more time he spent on the bottom, the more the likelihood there was of having to decompress when the job was finished. He didn't want to do that.

They went up slowly together and broke the surface forty feet from the barges.

"Glad you came looking for us," said Tom. "That's using the old head."

"What would you have done if I hadn't?" asked Chuck, out of curiosity.

"I'd have had to drag poor old Buzzie along the bottom of the ocean back to you to let you know we were going to surface."

"What happened to your mask?" Chuck asked.

"Dunno," said Buzzie. "Started leaking and I couldn't clear it. Water came in as fast as it was blown out. Must be leaking around the edge of the glass where it's sealed in the rubber."

"You're so tight-fisted you wouldn't spend five dollars on a new mask," said Tom. "Bet you've had that five years."

"Six," said Buzzie. "Bought it when you bought yours."

When they got to the barge they discovered that they had been on the bottom for fifteen minutes. In that time they had fastened three drums in place on the plane. They had nine more to place, which at the rate they were work-

[132]

ing, would mean forty-five minutes at twenty fathoms.

"Looks like we'll have to decompress," said Tom. He rummaged through his gear and produced a small watch-like instrument for calculating decompression times.

"One hour at twenty fathoms," he said. "That means we'll have to stop for thirteen minutes at thirty feet, twenty-eight minutes at twenty feet, and twenty-eight minutes at ten feet. No way out of it."

Tom looked at Chuck. "If you like, you can stay topside and Buzzie and I will finish off down there."

"Not a chance," said Chuck. "I'm going down and will decompress with you."

"O.K.," said Tom. "Might as well change tanks now. If we speed up the work on the bottom, we can get by without changing tanks under water. It should go faster now that we've got the hang of it anyway."

They put on fresh tanks and went down again.

XVI.

WHEN THEY REACHED the bottom again, the work went much faster for a while. The fifty-gallon drums were cumbersome to maneuver though they weighed no more at the bottom full of water than they would at the top empty. But the three divers developed a technique for handling them and in half an hour they had enough drums lashed to the foreward part of the plane to raise it if they were filled with air.

When the last drum was lashed in place, Chuck signaled Tom that he had to rest. He was feeling desperately tired. His limbs were heavy. He was breathing deeply and seemed unable to get sufficient air to refresh himself. He had occasional waves of nausea, which he had to fight against. The nausea, he realized, resulted from his constantly altering his position in the water, sometimes having to operate with his legs higher than his head, so that the blood ran into it.

He felt then that he needed to rest, and Tom nodded his agreement. They sat for a minute on the wing of the plane until Chuck's breathing had slowed down. Then Tom and Buzzie got the first of the lungs with which they would fill the drums with air.

They had brought a hose with a connection to it that would hook up to the valve on each lung. There had been some discussion as to whether they should use a regulator on the lung, which would reduce the pressure of the air as it came out of the lung to that of the surrounding water. But Buzzie had argued that this wasn't necessary. It would take longer for the drum to fill with air using a regulator, and if they just cracked the valve slightly, allowing a small stream of air to escape through the hose into the drum, the drum would fill more quickly and there would be no danger.

This, then, was what had been agreed on. Chuck put the open end of the high-pressure hose from the lung into the bunghole of the barrel and nodded. Tom cracked open the valve on the lung. Immediately there was a thundering sound from the drum as the air rushed out of the bunghole, signifying that that particular drum was full.

The next drum to be filled was the one occupying the same position on the opposite wing. While they were filling it, the wreckage shifted slightly, reacting to the upward pull of the air in the drums.

The noise of the air rushing into each drum as it displaced the water was appalling. It seemed to Chuck that the very violence of the sound would wreck the drums. He was closest to them, since it was his job to put the hose in the bunghole, while Tom and Buzzie handled the lungs.

[135]

He began to be afraid that one of the drums, though all were pressure tested, would explode in his face. It added to his fears that as each alternate drum was filled, the fuselage moved uneasily, tilting from one side to another.

When he got to the drums close to the engine housings, a black arm slowly appeared from under the wing of the plane and waved around with a groping motion before him. The arm, soft and slender, touched his wrist and then gripped it hard. It was the tentacle of an octopus that had taken up its home in the engine housing.

He jerked away instinctively, dropping the hose. The tentacle immediately gripped harder. Tom, seeing him struggling, went over to help. There were two loops of the tentacle around Chuck's arm, and he could feel the tightness of the grip even through the rubber of his wetsuit. In fact, he could almost feel the suction cups on his skin. The harder he pulled, the tighter the grip. He looked at Tom in panic. Tom was holding up his arms so that his forearms made right angles with his upperarms. That was the signal to hold still. Chuck relaxed and immediately he did so, his fears declined. Also the octopus, feeling the tug on his tentacles lessen, relaxed its grip, though only slightly.

"Why doesn't he cut me free?" Chuck wondered. Tom had a knife strapped to his leg and could cut the tentacle readily, but was making no attempt to use it. Then the octopus started to come out of the enginehouse. It flowed out, its soft body compressing itself to a few inches and coming through the aperture like a thick brown oil. It had two big eyes in the middle of its pulpy head and wasn't much bigger than a small dog. It looked sadly and disgustedly at Chuck, released Chuck's wrist, and, with a graceful and indignant flutter of its tentacles, took off. Chuck was almost ashamed of himself for nearly panick-

[136]

ing over something that looked so fearsome and yet was so harmless. They continued filling the drums.

When all but two of the drums had been filled, it was clear that the plane was about ready to leave the bottom. It was so light that the three of them could lift it up. Now was the time to signal the barge on the surface to be ready for the ascent.

Tom took a self-inflating float from his belt, pulled a string, and released it. The float was orange in color. It immediately started to fill with carbon dioxide gas and took off for the surface. They watched it going up, an orange balloon that disappeared from sight in the beautiful silvery sky above them that looked like so much quicksilver.

They then started filling the last two drums slowly. They filled them simultaneously, Chuck and Tom working on one and Buzzie on the other. This was necessary so that the plane would be balanced on its way up and would not take off with more floatation on one side than the other. The last two drums were under the wings, one on each side, and somewhat difficult to get at. Before they were full, the wreckage shifted, first slowly and then violently. One side of the fuselage broke clear of the bottom and then the other.

Tom and Chuck darted away and the whole assemblage started for the surface in a cloud of bubbles. Looking up they saw a storm of bubbles over their heads as, with the pressure decreasing during the ascent, the high-pressure air in the drums escaped.

Chuck looked around for Buzzie. During the filling of the last two drums Buzzie had been hidden from them by the fuselage. He was nowhere to be seen.

Then Tom spotted him surrounded by a whirling cloud

of bubbles and apparently hooked to the plane. Tom shot off from the bottom immediately with Chuck following. But before they had risen twenty feet, Buzzie came down to meet them. He pointed to his weight belt, signaling that one of the weights had become hooked in the last few seconds on a jagged piece of the fuselage. He formed a circle with his thumb and forefinger to signal that he was O.K., and the three of them returned to the bottom glancing upward all the time lest anything happen to the wreckage that would start it down again.

They had to wait now for a signal that the wreckage was safely on the surface and hooked to the barge. Then decompression lines would be sent to them and another line on which they could tie their gear so it could be hauled up to the barge.

The gear line came down first, and they tied on the empty lungs they had used, and it was hauled back to the surface. Attached to it was a piece of white plastic board carrying the following words in black grease pencil:

"Wreckage secured. 13 at 30 feet. 28 at 20. 28 at 10. Sending lines. Love Shirley."

The figures, Chuck knew, referred to the amount of time they would have to spend decompressing at the different depths. This was to allow the liquid nitrogen which had accumulated in the blood stream to become gas and escape through their lungs. Otherwise they would get the "bends."

Shirley's note meant spending something more than an hour under water hanging motionless on lines. Chuck tried to figure whether he would have enough air left or would have to change tanks underwater. He concluded that he would have to change tanks. But Tom and Buzzie would be there to help him so it wouldn't be too bad.

[138]

A few minutes later the three lines on which they were to decompress came down. They secured them to the bottom. They had kept three lungs, fitted with regulators, on the bottom for emergency use. Each took one and started up the decompression lines.

When they got to the first decompression level, thirty feet from the surface, they found a sling in the line made of rope like a bosun's chair. Chuck thrust his legs through the sling with great difficulty because of his flippers and sat in it. Tom looked at his watch, and they settled down to sweat out the first stage of their decompression.

"We're just like three lumps of bait hung on the end of a fishing line," Chuck thought. Then he put that thought quickly aside for it had unpleasant associations.

XVII.

DECOMPRESSING WAS WORSE than Chuck had imagined it would be. The cold was the hardest to endure. Working on the bottom and in his wetsuit, he had been comfortably warm. He began to notice the cold, however, in the first few minutes of decompression. Obliged to remain motionless on the line, first his feet, then his hands began to hurt. The pain of the cold seeped through his muscles and bones.

He could do something to relieve it by moving his feet and hands, but this became very tiring after a while. The cold was particularly intense in the region of his back over his kidneys. The weight of his belt was impeding circulation. He loosened the belt a little and got some relief. But the cold continued to seep through his limbs, and he was soon shivering with it.

After the cold, there was a sense of nausea to deal with.

He tried to discover the reason for his nausea and decided it came from being suspended in space with no landmarks about to give him a sense of position. At thirty feet from the surface he could not see the bottom, ninety feet below. Looking outward there was only the vague obscurity of the ocean. When he looked up, he could see the mirror of the surface, so bright that it almost hurt his eyes.

The barge had moved off, towing the wreckage of the plane to the harbor. So their job was done. But Chuck felt no great satisfaction over it. The barge had been replaced by a launch to which the lines were attached. He wondered whether Shirley was on the launch, and decided that she probably was.

He could not keep looking up for long because he got a crick in his neck. Tom and Buzzie clung to their lines close by but after exchanging a few signals there was no communication among them. An hour had to be spent in this manner then, sitting in silence and in space, with nothing to do.

The first thirteen minutes at thirty feet went slowly enough. But the twenty-eight minutes that followed at twenty feet seemed interminable. The sling cut into Chuck's legs. When he got out of the sling to relieve them, his hands hurt from hanging on the decompression line. He would have given anything to move about, but he had to remain where he was.

He fell to pondering on the color of the ocean. Nearby it was the palest of green, if it had any color at all. Below it became a muddy color somewhere between green and brown. That was strange because he remembered when they started work on the bottom, there had been shafts of sunlight coming down to the reef. He decided that the sky had clouded up. As he stared into the distance, the pale

[141]

green turned to a moss green beyond which he could not see. There were no fish to watch. Chuck thought that was curious. Every time he dived he had seen plenty of fish but there were none now. He began to think over the details of the salvage job.

He was almost amused at his apprehensions. He had expected some terrible ordeal under water, and everything had gone without a hitch. He had, of course, been terrified when the octopus had put a tentacle around him. But everything unexpected was frightening under water. At least, such things frightened him, though Tom and Buzzie took them calmly enough. Buzzie hadn't panicked when his face plate broke at twenty fathoms. And he hadn't panicked when he got hooked to the wreckage as it ascended.

That was the great thing to remember when submerged —don't panic. Something Tom had said to him once returned to his mind. It was: ''Panic can turn a good swimmer into a non-swimmer in one second.'' That was true. Panic came out of fear and it deprived a man of all his skills and abilities. It was, as Tom had also said, the greatest monster of the deep.

Chuck looked over at Tom, dangling on his line ten feet away. He was resting his head against the line to which he was suspended and seemed to be asleep. The air bubbles from his regulator rose in regular clouds showing that he was breathing easily. Good old Tom. Nothing panicked him either under the water or above it. Maybe he got frightened for a moment, but he was master of himself.

The waiting, the silence, and the cold began to oppress Chuck more and more. How much longer would he have to stay down there suspended on the line? Forty minutes? Fifty minutes? He had no idea. Forty minutes waiting on

[142]

land in the sunshine was nothing. But forty minutes under water seemed an eternity. The best thing to do was think of something else.

He thought about his father. It occurred to him that he might be wrong in thinking his father a failure because of his modest position in the world. Whatever his father had, he had achieved himself. That was no small success in itself. He was respected and well liked. He owned his home and his paint store. He had started out with very little education and no influence and had made himself independent. Chuck couldn't even guess at the reverses his father had met in establishing his business. He had never even thought of his father having any reverses, but he thought of this now.

There must have been many nights when his father lay awake worrying about money problems. This had never occurred to Chuck before, and he was ashamed of having been so insensitive. Why had he thought of it now, he wondered? Maybe it was because of his experience in diving. Every step he had taken in learning to dive had called for a distinct effort of will and a distinct exertion of courage. So in a sense learning to dive was like learning to deal with the world. No matter how much people wanted to help you, the decisions lay with yourself and the courage to carry out decisions came from yourself. No one could supply you with either decision or courage. Your mind and your character were entirely your own.

He had learned it from the ocean. He'd found out something else, too. Tom and Buzzie had trusted him as partners on the salvage job. In no small sense they had been willing to put their lives in his hands. That was a great measure of trust. If they trusted him, why did he so often doubt himself? Wasn't he selling himself short far too

[143]

many times? When he got into fits of depression about his future, wasn't he allowing himself to be panicked by phantoms that didn't even exist?

"I've been like Shirley," Chuck said to himself. "I've let fear get the better of me and even prevent me from trying. She won't go diving again because she had one bad experience. She's run by fears. But I've been ridden by fears and doubts without even having a bad experience."

From this train of thought Chuck switched to his air supply. He tried to calculate whether he would need to change his lung or not. He endeavored to assure himself that he would have enough air to avoid it.

"Maybe I'll be almost out when the decompression time is through but I'll have enough," he said. Then he knew he was kidding himself because he was afraid to change lungs under water. He had done it in a swimming pool, but never in the ocean. He knew the technique, and yet he was still apprehensive.

"O.K.," he said to himself, "if I have to change lungs, why not do it now and get it over with?" He was using a single hose regulator and his spare tank was equipped with a double hose regulator. That made it awkward to put on below the surface. He started to think the steps out.

First he must turn on the valve of the spare unit. Then he must hold the mouthpiece of the spare down below the tank itself so the air would not escape from it. That meant when he put the mouthpiece in place there would be water in it, for the two-hose unit, unlike the single hose, had no button for automatically clearing the water out of the hose. He must have sufficient air left in his lungs to clear the water out of the hose of the spare by blowing.

No. There was a better way. He could hold the mouthpiece of the spare up above the tank when he turned on the valve and the air would start coming out and clear the hose automatically. He would lose some air but it was the safer way to do it. Before doing anything else, however, he ought to get out of the harness of the tank he was using.

Having cleared up the steps to be taken in his own mind, he signaled to Buzzie and Tom that he was going to change tanks by beating on his chest. Tom was about to come over to him to help, but Chuck gave him the O.K. signal indicating that he could manage by himself.

The spare lung was fastened to the line just below him. He first undid the two buckles holding the lung he was using to his back. It was now held in place by only one shoulder strap, out of which he could slip when he was ready. He got out of his sling and went down two feet so that he was opposite the spare lung. It was held by one of its harness straps through a loop in the line. He loosened it and immediately was confronted with a very obvious difficulty which he had not foreseen. He had the spare lung in one hand and was holding on to the decompression line with the other. Without three hands, how was he to open the valve on the spare lung?

He solved the problem by wrapping the decompression line around his leg so that he was held to it. With his one free hand, he opened the value on the spare lung. Immediately there was a tremendous surge of bubbles from the mouthpiece which rushed past his face blinding him. He was never quite sure what happened next. He had undone the strap holding in place the mouthpiece of the lung he was using. He made an impulsive grab for the mouthpiece of the spare out of which the air was rushing at such tremendous speed and the lung on his back slipped off his

[145]

shoulder, though it was still held by its strap in the crook of his arm.

He was overcome by a terrible dread of dropping both lungs and with his air supply gone, drowning. But the near-panic lasted for but a second. He worked the shoulder strap back into place on his shoulder, took the mouthpiece of the spare and brought it over his head so that the two hoses came over his shoulders. He could not see because of the air bubbles escaping from the lung. He searched by feeling for the shoulder strap on the spare lung but could not find it with all the bubbles about. Again he had a feeling of panic, and again he mastered it. The way to stop the bubbles was to let go of the mouthpiece of the lung he was using and put the mouthpiece of the spare in his mouth.

He did so deliberately. He had to hold his breath for only a second during this interchange and felt enormously relieved when he found he could get air from the spare lung once the mouthpiece was in place. Now there were no panicking air bubbles to deal with and he got into the harness of the spare without further fear. The whole operation had probably taken no more than a minute. It seemed to Chuck to have lasted half an hour. There was only one thing more to do—turn off the air on the discarded unit.

When he had done all this, he looked around and found that Buzzie was holding on to the decompression line just below him. If he had panicked, Buzzie would have been standing by to help him. He was enormously grateful. But he was even more pleased that he hadn't needed help, that he had been able to take care of the whole operation himself.

[146]

Buzzie returned to his own line and he and Tom changed their tanks. Buzzie changed first and then Tom. Tom stood guard on Buzzie during the operation and Chuck, having secured the discarded tank to his decompression line, stood guard on Tom. When this was done, it was time to go up to the ten-foot level. There were only twenty-eight minutes more to spend in decompressing.

The last decompression period went faster. For one thing the water was warmer. Then Shirley started to send down notes to them on a weighted line. The notes were written on plastic with a grease pencil as she had done before. The first one read:

"Got any matches?" Another said, "Sending down evening paper so you can do the crossword."

When this message came, Chuck took the piece of plastic and, getting a grease pencil from Tom, wrote on it, "Bring paper down yourself—Chuck."

He meant it as a joke but he hoped when the line had gone up that it would not cut too close to Shirley's fear. It didn't. Back came a message reading: "Not likely—Shirley." To this Chuck replied, "Lonely down here. Come on and visit. Water's lovely."

There was no reply to this message for a long time, and Chuck wondered whether he had offended Shirley. He reasoned that if she could take a little ribbing about her fears, then she was that much closer to overcoming them. And it was important for her to overcome them.

When ten minutes had elapsed without a reply to his message he concluded gloomily that Shirley was offended. Then there was a splash above them and Shirley came swimming down toward them.

She made directly for the line to which Chuck was clinging and had the piece of plastic in her hand. She held it up before Chuck's mask. On it was written, "I came down to tell you that you're a pig—but a nice pig."

He reached out and took her hand. It felt very small. But it also felt as if that was where it belonged—in his.

XVIII.

TWO WEEKS LATER Tom and Chuck came back from a pleasure dive off Redondo Beach. They had been down looking for lobsters on the seaward side of the breakwater and had got four each. Tom had also filled a small bag with various-sized weights and fishhooks lost by anglers fishing from the breakwater. Chuck had brought back a piece of stone, beautifully striped in bands of black and white which he had found on the bottom. It would make a fine addition to the collection of stones he had previously picked up on the beach before he had learned to scuba dive.

Tired from their diving, they took off their weight belts and tanks and sat for a while on the beach looking out at the ocean. They were in the same place where Tom had first suggested to Chuck that he might like to learn to dive. That seemed to Chuck to have been several years ago.

"How do you like your new wetsuit?" asked Tom.

"Swell," said Chuck. "Somehow it makes a difference when you own all your own gear." He had bought a complete outfit from Dive 'N Surf with the money he had received for his part in the salvage of the plane.

The two of them sat for a while in silence watching the waves break and come hissing up toward them. Chuck was thinking of the ocean. What a tremendous world lay beneath its glittering blue surface. It was a world of silence and inexpressible beauty. It was also a world of menace and fear. Beauty and menace lay side by side beneath the ocean and he was not sure which of these two qualities attracted him the most. But the attraction was there. It was irresistible, and he knew that for the rest of his life, as long as he was physically able, he would be diving into the enchanting submarine world, seeing more and more of its loveliness and never tiring of it.

"Things are a bit different from the last time you and I were sitting here," said Tom at length.

"Yes," agreed Chuck.

"You were a pretty mixed-up kid then, weren't you?"

"Yes," replied Chuck, "I couldn't seem to get straightened out. I was full of hope and then fear and wanted to be alone and think. But thinking didn't seem to do me any good. But that's all changed now. The ocean changed it."

"Got any idea how?" asked Tom with a half-smile.

"I don't know whether I can tell you," said Chuck. "It is the beauty that is in the ocean and the fear that is in it too. You get down in the loveliness and the fearfulness and you seem to grow, and things get into a better perspective. That's the only way I can explain it."

"When you're diving," said Tom slowly, "you get a kind of miniature view of the whole of living in about one

[150]

hour under water. People give you all sorts of advice, but you're strictly alone. No one can dive for you, and no one can live for you. Friends can do all they can to help you. But in the showdown you have to do the job yourself."

"For a long time, if I could have found a way of backing out without losing face, I'd have called off those diving lessons," said Chuck.

"I know," said Tom. "And for a long time if you could have found a way of backing out, you'd have put off facing the world, and trying out how good you are in it. But I figured if you went through with the lessons, you wouldn't have much trouble adjusting to the world and learning how to get along without being full of despair one minute and full of hope the next; and you'd learn to understand others, like your father, and the struggles they've had to face alone. Then you wouldn't think anybody was a failure, however small their position in the world. Diving taught you something of your own worth and other people's worth. Now you don't have to be full of self-doubts any longer."

"I wouldn't have gone ahead with the diving if it hadn't been for Shirley," said Chuck. "She shamed me into it."

"Well, you evened the score by getting her to overcome her own fears and go down again," said Tom.

"I always had a feeling that there was something in the ocean waiting for me to find," said Chuck. "I didn't know what it was, except that it belonged to me and I must find it. Turned out to be what I found in the ocean was myself. Is that why you suggested teaching me to dive?"

"Figure it out for yourself," said Tom, getting up. "Come on, it's getting hot in this suit. Let's go and change."

They picked up their gear and staggered with it across

[151]

the beach to the lifeguard headquarters. Shirley met them on the way. Without a word she took Chuck's weight belt from him, and they went on together. They were to dive together the following week off one of the offshore islands. They would go down together through the beautiful golden kelp that rose seventy feet in a forest of sheer delight through the blue depths of the ocean.

Chuck was glad she was going to be with him. She had given him the courage to go ahead with something of which he was afraid. And he in return had given her the courage to overcome her own fear.

He hoped they would be together for the rest of their lives. He thought about that for a moment and knew, beyond any doubt, that they would. Life was good and he was anxious to meet it and live it out with her.

F
OCO
O'CONNOR, PATRICK
Treasure at twenty
fathoms

DATE DUE			
		ALESCO	